The Canadian Spelling Program 2.1

6

Ruth Scott
Sharon Siamon

gagelearning

We acknowledge the financial support of the Government of Canada through the Book Publishing Industry Development Program for our publishing activities.

Canadian Cataloguing in Publication Data

Scott, Ruth, 1949

The Canadian spelling program 2.1, 6

ISBN 0-7715-1584-7

1. Spellers. 2. English language - Orthography and spelling - Problems, exercises, etc. I. Siamon, Sharon. II. Title.

PE1145.2.S37 1996   428.1   C95-932182-9

Design: Pronk&Associates

Illustration: Graham Bardell, Shirley Clemmer,Tony Kew

Cover Photograph: Dave Starrett

The authors and publisher gratefully acknowledge the contributions of the following educators to *The Canadian Spelling Program 2.1:*

Lynn Archer
Surrey, British Columbia

Judith MacManus
Riverview, New Brunswick

Sylvia Arnold
Aurora, Ontario

Denis Maika
Mississauga, Ontario

Carol Chandler
Halifax, Nova Scotia

Bill Nimigon
North York, Ontario

Linda Hollowell
North York, Ontario

Gordon Williamson
Winnipeg, Manitoba

Caroline Lutyk
Burlington, Ontario

ISBN 0-7715-**1584-7**

 9 10 11   GG   04 03 02

Written, Printed, and Bound in Canada.

CONTENTS

▼▼▼

How to Study Your Words

You will already know how to spell some of the words in this book, but there might be some words that are hard for you.

When you need to study a word, use these steps:
1. **Look** at the word, letter by letter.
2. **Say** the word to yourself, listening carefully.
3. **Cover** the word.
4. **Write** the word.
5. **Check** the spelling, letter by letter, with the word in the list.

If you make a mistake, notice where it is. Did you make a mistake at the beginning of the word, or in the middle, or at the end? Was your mistake with a consonant letter, or a vowel letter, or both?

Now do all the steps over again with the same word.

Dictionary Symbols

Look at these symbols: /a/ /ē/ /är/ /k/.

Symbols like these stand for sounds. For example, the symbol /a/ stands for the short vowel **a** you hear at the beginning of **a**pple. You will find these symbols in the dictionary and other books about words.

New Words

The new words in this spelling book may come from the areas of technology, from culture, or they may simply be old words with new meanings. You will probably find many others you can add to the list.

Preferred Spelling

You will notice that some words spelled with **or** in the first edition of this book (**color, favorite, neighbor**) are spelled **our** in this revised edition (**colour, favourite, neighbour**). The **our** spelling is now considered the preferred Canadian spelling.

1 Short Vowel Review

bat bet bit
blot but

unless
skill
bomb
except
lock
pocket
smash
trick
check
depth
craft
half
grand
contest
lift
switch
understand
puzzle

The Magician

This is Beverley Windsor for Kids' Report reporting live from the finals of the magicians' <u>contest</u>. We're about to see the <u>grand</u> finale of Murdo the Magnificent. She's going to toss a live firecracker into her top hat. If Murdo can make this <u>trick</u> work it will be a <u>smash</u> hit. If she can't, she'll <u>bomb</u> (if you'll pardon the pun!).

We've already seen Murdo perform one amazing trick after another in the last <u>half</u> hour. We've seen her break a watch in pieces, then hand it back, in perfect order, to its owner. We've seen her escape from locked chains in a tank filled with water to a <u>depth</u> of six metres. I tested the <u>lock</u> myself, and it was tight! Murdo has done everything in her act <u>except</u> pull a live rabbit from a hat.

Now, she's lighting the fuse on the firecracker. I'd like to <u>check</u> what Murdo has in her <u>pocket</u>, or up her sleeve. She's putting the firecracker in her hat. Now she's starting to <u>lift</u> something out of her hat. It's a live rabbit! I know Murdo is a magician of great <u>craft</u> and <u>skill</u>, but I don't <u>understand</u>. How did she <u>switch</u> that firecracker for a rabbit? It's a <u>puzzle</u>.

This is Beverley Windsor signing off for Kids' Report.

Observing Patterns

1. Write the seven list words that begin with a consonant blend.

Example: ***fr**iend* ***bl**ock*

2. Write the list words that match these shapes.

3. Write the list words in alphabetical order that would be found on a dictionary page headed by each set of guide words.

   a) pleasant / pyramid
   b) uncover / until
   c) carnival / customer
   d) load / lucky

Discovering Patterns

unless skill bomb except lock pocket smash trick check depth craft half grand contest lift switch understand puzzle

1. a) The list words all contain short vowels. Make a chart in your notebook like the one below. Then sort the list words into the correct categories.

/a/ as in **track**	/e/ as in **echo**	/i/ as in **pickle**	/o/ as in **stocking**	/u/ as in **summer**

b) Add two more words to each column which fit the patterns.

Hint! If a word has more than one short vowel, place it in the chart according to the first vowel.

POWERBOOSTER

• The short vowel sound /a/ is usually spelled with the letter **a**; /e/ with **e**; /i/ with **i**; /o/ with **o**; /u/ with **u**.

Exploring Patterns

1. Spin the wheel to match short vowels with words on the outer circle. Each time you can make a real word, score a point.

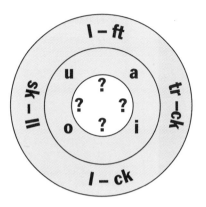

2. Many of the list words have more than one meaning. Write the list word that matches each set of definitions.

_____ **a)** to find out or investigate; a mark to show correct or incorrect; a pattern made of squares

_____ **b)** a trade or some kind of work requiring special skill; an article made by hand

_____ **c)** change direction; a device for turning lights on and off

_____ **d)** a means of fastening doors, boxes; an enclosed section of a canal; a curl or ringlet of hair

3. Pull the correct letters out of the hat to complete these list words.

de _ th	swi _ ch	ex _ e _ t
ha _ f	_ om _	pu _ _ le

4. Perform some word magic! Complete the word pole with words that fit the definitions.

a) _ _ |**l**| _   divided into two equal parts
b) _ _ |**l**| _   offspring of a cow
c) _ _ |**l**| _   opposite of rough, stormy
d) _ _ |**l**| _   inside of the hand

Many of these words have consonants that are silent or hard to hear.

3

5. In this book we will be writing about transformations in the worlds of nature, technology, sports, and the arts. Transformers change one thing to another.

a) Work in a group and brainstorm about the topic of **transformation**. Spin off ideas around the web.

b) When you have finished get together with other groups and compare webs. Did you have the same ideas.

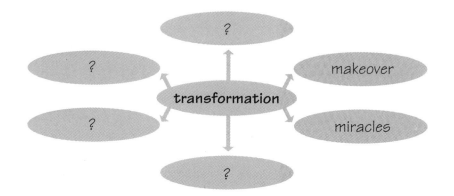

Challenges with Words

1. Choose a Super Word that completes each set of synonyms below.

a) conjuror, illusionist, trickster, _____

b) extreme, tremendous, incredible, _____

c) mysterious, baffling, curious, _____

d) masterful, capable, proficient, _____

e) participant, contender, competitor, _____

f) vanish, fade, depart, _____

2. Write each set of words in exercise 1, including the Super Words, in order from weakest to strongest.

Example: depart, fade, disappear, vanish

Compare your lists with a partner's. Did you agree on the order?

fantastic
skilful
contestant
magician
disappear
puzzling

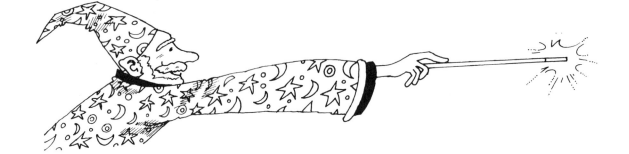

3. Word Magic: By changing only one letter at a time, a word can be transformed into a new word. **Told** can be transformed into **boat** in **3** steps.

told → **b**old → bol**t** → boat

Now try these transformations.

a) **fan**tastic—transform the **fan** in **fantastic** into something a man wears around his neck (3 steps)

b) disap**pear**ance—transform the **pear** in **disappearance** into a place a bird lives (3 steps)

c) con**test**ant—transform the **test** in **contestant** into a large animal that likes honey (3 steps)

4. Which Super Word can be spelled in two different ways? What other words can you think of that have two spellings?

5. Words can be transformed by adding **suffixes**. Look carefully at these words.

disappearance   contestant   magician

a) Make a list of the base words in the words above. Then list the suffixes that have been added.

b) Choose suffixes from your list to transform these words.

assist annoy library serve history

c) Circle the letter that changed in each word when you added a suffix.

6. Make a word web for any one of the Super Words. Using the ideas and words on your web, write a short report or story about that topic.

Example:

full   empty

money ← **pocket** → spy

button ←   → secret

zip   book

7. These new words come from the ever-changing world of video and computer games. Unscramble the words in the sentences below.

a) We use a <u>yjo cksit</u> to make the characters move.

b) My brother and sister spend hours in the <u>dvoie dercaa</u>.

c) We can use a <u>nrlocot dpa</u> with our computer game instead of a keyboard or a mouse.

NEW WORDS

joy stick
control pad
video arcade

5

2 Long Vowel Review

vowel–consonant–e

bake bike

whole
complete
larva
nectar
lonely
extreme
pupa
adult
scale
provide
compete
quote
stroke
migrate
widely
stage
escape
prize

The Caterpillar

This is Nigel DeBarlo with a live nature report. We're about to witness one of the most amazing transformations in the <u>whole</u> world of nature. Can the caterpillar, that <u>lonely</u> <u>larva</u>, <u>escape</u> from its <u>pupa</u> prison? We can see the pupa beginning to split near the top. What will emerge slowly is a <u>complete</u> <u>adult</u> monarch butterfly.

At this <u>stage</u> of the monarch's life cycle, <u>nectar</u> will <u>provide</u> the nourishment it needs to mate, lay eggs, and <u>migrate</u> great distances from the <u>extreme</u> cold of Canadian winters. Now the monarch's crumpled wings are beginning to emerge. They spread more <u>widely</u> with each <u>stroke</u>. Soon each tiny wing <u>scale</u> will glitter in the sunlight. The monarch can <u>compete</u> with any butterfly to win a <u>prize</u> for grace and beauty.

There it goes! To <u>quote</u> from a famous song, it must be great to 'float like a butterfly'.

Observing Patterns

1. Write the list words that have two syllables. Place an accent (´) on the syllable that is stressed.

Example: **mí grate**

Which two-syllable word could have the accent placed on either syllable? Hint! This person is older than you.

2. Write in alphabetical order the five single-syllable list words that would fall between the words **prison** and **structure** in the dictionary.

prison, _____ , _____ , _____

_____ , _____ , structure

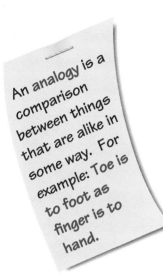

An analogy is a comparison between things that are alike in some way. For example: Toe is to foot as finger is to hand.

3. Write the five list words that begin with consonant blends (each consonant is sounded).

4. a) Complete each analogy with a list word.
   some is to **all** as **part** is to _____
   colt is to **horse** as **child** is to _____
   wine is to **grapes** as **honey** is to _____
   find is to **lose** as **keep** is to _____
   b) Create two more sets of analogies that can be completed by list words. Try these on a partner.

Discovering Patterns

whole complete larva nectar lonely extreme pupa adult scale provide compete quote stroke migrate widely stage escape prize

1. Each of the following list words contains a long vowel.
   stage   extreme   prize   whole
   a) Write each word and underline the letters that spell the long vowel sound.
   b) Describe the vowel and consonant spelling pattern in each word.

2. a) Sort the list words with long vowels into the categories below.

/ā/ spelled a-consonant-e	/ē/ spelled e-consonant-e	/ī/ spelled i-consonant-e	/ō/ spelled o-consonant-e
scale			

   b) Add two more words which fit the patterns to each column.

POWERBOOSTER

- The **vowel-consonant-e** pattern spells the long vowel sound in many words.

Exploring Patterns

1. Combine the letters around the butterfly's wings with any of the **vowel-consonant-e** patterns to form words with the long vowel sound. Score one point for each word you make.

Example: **a c e**

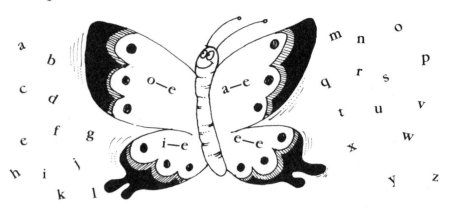

2. Many of the list words can be used as base words to build other words. The new words formed will be similar in meaning to the base. Complete the sentences below by using the correct form of the words.

a) The _____ temperatures in the Arctic make life there _____ difficult.   (extreme extremity extremely)

b) Monarch butterflies _____ thousands of kilometres south in the winter. By tagging the butterflies, scientists can study their _____ patterns.   (migrate migrant migration)

3. Complete the following sentences with words that are made from the base word **compete**. Use a dictionary to check the spelling of the new words formed.

a) The first event was a diving **com**_____ .
b) Each **com**_____ completed three dives.
c) The swimmers were very **com**_____ because they all wanted to capture first prize.

4. Complete the list words on each caterpillar.

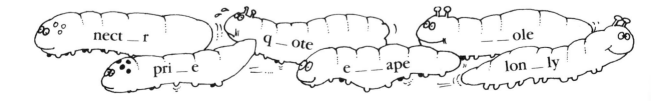

nect _ r

pri _ e

q _ ote

e _ _ ape

_ _ ole

lon _ ly

In Greek mythology, **nectar** was known as the drink of the gods. The word **nectar** comes from the Greek words <u>nek</u> meaning 'death' and <u>tar</u> meaning 'conquering'.

5. What did the ancient Greeks think would happen to anyone who drank nectar?

6. You receive this letter from your six-year-old cousin, Rosa.

Dear Cousin,

I am so sad because my caterpillar Ralph is gone. In his jar there is a hard green thing. Should I bust it open to find Ralph?

Rosa

Write back, explaining why she shouldn't break open the pupa or chrysalis. Explain what has happened to Ralph, and what will happen if she waits patiently.

Reread your letter carefully to check whether you have made your points clearly. Ralph's life is on the line!

Challenges with Words

1. Use Super Words to replace their synonyms in the paragraph below.

Many **kinds** of butterflies hibernate in their **chrysalises** to escape the cold. A long, **annual journey** is very difficult for such **delicate** creatures. Two life **rotations** are necessary for some monarch butterflies to complete their 3200 kilometre trip. Female monarchs lay eggs along the way. The offspring, after their **transformation** into adults, continue the northward journey.

migration
cycles
fragile
metamorphosis
species
pupae

2. a) Sounds Good! Identify the Super Words using only the **sound** clues. Then, unscramble the letters in brackets to spell a word that fits the sentence below.

I have two long **e** sounds. (_) _ _ _ _ _ _
I have a long **a** and a long **i**. _ _ _ _ (_) _ _ _ _
I have a short **e** and a short **i**. _ _ _ _ _ _ _ _ _ _ (_) _ _
I have a long **u** and a long **i**. _ _ _ _ (_)
I have a long **i** and a short **a**. _ _ _ _ _ (_) _
I have a long **i** and the same letter with two
different sounds. (_) _ _ _ _ _
The _____ on my wings are beautiful things.

3. Peculiar Plurals: Most words in English make the plural form by adding **s**. A few end in **a** and add an **e**, such as—**pupae**. Make the following words plural.

larva antenna alga pupa

4. Some words can only be used as plurals.

Example: **species series**

Can you find other words that are always plural? Fit some into these sentences.

a) I can't see. I've lost my _____ .
b) Cut the paper with those _____ .
c) I need _____ to bend those wires.
d) The spy ring had its _____ in an old office building.

5. We call things 'as light as a feather'. Why not 'as light as a butterfly'? When you write, you can use comparisons to make your writing clearer and more interesting. Make a chart like the one below and write words in each column which suggest **lightness**. Then write a short description about one of the people or things listed in your chart.

Things	Actions	Descriptive Words
moth	flit	delicate

Long a Long e

ai ay eigh ee ea y

maintain display sleigh
creep really

maintain
between
propeller
creep
explain
season
proceed
cushion
stray
release
freight
scurry
display
really
sleigh
hurry
weigh
bury

The Hovercraft

This is Amy Wong reporting from beautiful British Columbia. I've just seen a <u>display</u> of the <u>really</u> incredible power of a Canadian Coast Guard rescue hovercraft.

The hovercraft can be transformed from a boat to a land vehicle instantly. It can <u>proceed</u> anywhere, in any <u>season</u>. It can <u>creep</u> across mud flats or <u>scurry</u> over the crests of waves, without even pausing <u>between</u> land and water. Any normal boat hitting the shore at high speed would <u>bury</u> its nose in mud, but the hovercraft rides over mud, rocks, or swamp. This makes it possible for the hovercraft pilot to <u>hurry</u> to the rescue of a <u>stray</u> hiker stranded on a tidal flat, or a small boat drifting helplessly with a broken <u>propeller</u>.

Let me try to <u>explain</u> briefly how a hovercraft works. Its powerful engines <u>release</u> and <u>maintain</u> a <u>cushion</u> of air under the craft. Though the hovercraft must <u>weigh</u> many tonnes, it 'flies' on this air like a <u>sleigh</u> over snow. It can carry heavy <u>freight</u> or passengers, as well as performing rescue work.

I'd better hurry and catch my hovercraft back to the mainland. This is Amy Wong, signing off for Kids' Report.

Observing Patterns

1. Write the four list words that contain double consonants.

2. Complete each set of words with a list word.
   a) crawl, slither, slide, _____
   b) pad, soften, relieve, _____
   c) intermediate, middle, medium, _____
   d) wing, fuselage, tail, _____
   e) cover, conceal, hide, _____
   f) autumn, winter, spring, _____

3. Write the four list words that rhyme with **today**.

4. Write the list words that fit these definitions.
   a) to tell what something means or how something is done
   b) to keep in good condition
   c) load of goods carried on a train, ship, and so on
   d) to move forward; carry on an activity
   e) to let go

Discovering Patterns

maintain between propeller creep explain season proceed cushion stray release freight scurry display really sleigh hurry weigh bury

1. a) Many of the list words contain the long vowel sound /ā/ as in **train**, **stay**, or **eight**. Make a chart in your notebook like the one below. Sort each list word with the sound /ā/ into the correct category.

/ā/ spelled **ai**	/ā/ spelled **ay**	/ā/ spelled **eigh**

Sorting words into the correct categories will help you remember their spelling patterns.

   b) Add one other word which fits the pattern to each column.

2. a) Other list words contain the long vowel sound /ē/ as in **tree**, **bean**, or **any**. Sort the list words with the sound /ē/ into the categories below.

/ē/ spelled **ee**	/ē/ spelled **ea**	/ē/ spelled **y**

   b) Add one other word to each column which fits the patterns.

POWERBOOSTER

- The long vowel sound /ā/ may be spelled **ai** as in **train**, **ay** as in **stay**, or **eigh** as in **eight**.
- The long vowel sound /ē/ may be spelled **ee** as in **tree**, **ea** as in **bean**, or **y** as in **any**.

Exploring Patterns

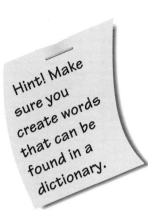

Hint! Make sure you create words that can be found in a dictionary.

1. Combine the letters from each set of cogs to create as many words with the long **a** or **e** sound as you can. Score 1 point for each word you make.

Example: strait   *Example: cream*

2. Three of the list words are **homophones**: words that sound the same but have different meanings and sometimes different spellings. Complete each pair of sentences using the correct homophone.

way   **a)** How much does that basket of apples _____?

weigh   **b)** Do you know the correct _____ to operate this equipment?

slay   **c)** The people in the village hoped the knight would _____ the dragon.

sleigh   **d)** I love to take horse-drawn _____ rides in the winter.

berry   **e)** Be sure to _____ your trash at the campsite.

bury   **f)** What type of _____ is on this bush?

3. What happens when **-es** and **-ed** are added to base words which end in a **consonant** + **y**?

Example: party-parties   marry-married

Complete the chart below by adding **-es** and **-ed** to the base words.

Base Word	-es	-ed
bury	_____	_____
hurry	_____	_____
scurry	_____	_____

4. Repair the broken words in the first column with the replacement word parts from the second column.

Broken Words	Parts
prope____er	shion
pr__c__d	eigh
fr___t	r
bu__y	rr
hu___y	ll
cu_____	o ee

5. It's a challenge trying to work the list words into a story or report. It's also fun. Try it and see for yourself. Use as many list words as you can in your own story. Here are some suggested topics:

- a science display
- a kind of aircraft
- an adventure on the water
- a strange and wonderful dream

When you've finished your writing share it with a classmate. Be sure to proofread your work carefully.

Challenges with Words

1. Use the Super Words to fill in the blanks in the paragraph from the hovercraft pilot's personal log.

At 17:00 hours, the rescue _____ was called out for the _____ time that day. Two young boys were stranded at the bottom of a cliff and the tide was coming in fast. We pushed our craft to its top _____ , hoping to get there on time. The rough _____ was no problem for our hovercraft, and we picked up the boys at 17:22. After a day like this, it's _____ to expect that our craft will need some _____ before we go out on another mission.

2. Write the next paragraph in the pilot's diary or log. Describe another rescue mission the same day, from the point of view of the hovercraft pilot.

eighth
maintenance
terrain
hovercraft
reasonable
velocity

3. Synonym Hunt: Think of three **synonyms** for the Super Words **terrain** and **velocity**. Then, replace the underlined words in the sentences below with the synonym that best fits each one. Use a dictionary or thesaurus to help you.

a) The <u>terrain</u> was the roughest I'd ever seen.

b) It seemed to fly at the <u>velocity</u> of light.

4. All Aboard! Many names of vehicles are compound words such as **hovercraft**. Make as many compound words as you can by combining the words in the box with one another.

craft	sail	street	board
surf	car	cycle	motor
skate	ship	steam	boat

5. What's your favourite mode of transportation? Choose one of the compound words you made in the question above, and describe what you like to do with it. You could also describe an invention of your own, such as a **steamboard** or a **surfcycle**. Draw a sketch of your invention. You may want to start your description like this: The surfcycle is my favourite vehicle because it combines pedal power with wind power and....

6. The new words come from the world of transportation. Complete each sentence below with the correct new word.

a) 'Father Goose' studied migrating geese with his _____ .

b) You can drive from Great Britain to France through the _____ .

c) A _____ uses special blades to move quickly across the surface of the water.

ultralight aircraft

chunnel

hydrofoil

4 Long e Long i Long o

ie igh oa ow o
bel**ie**ve br**igh**t

believe
toast
heavy
below
piece
bowl
coast
marble
unload
ocean
relief
growth
slight
photo
bright
opening
frighten
patio

Marvellous Marble

Hi everybody! This is Alexander Douglas for Kids' Report. <u>Believe</u> it or not, I'm standing on what was once the <u>coast</u> of an ancient <u>ocean</u>. This huge <u>opening</u> in the earth is a <u>marble</u> quarry. Thousands of years ago the shells of sea creatures built up layers of limestone <u>below</u> the surface. Heat and pressure have transformed the soft limestone into dense, <u>heavy</u> marble, used for everything from <u>patio</u> steps to marble statues.

The quarry I'm visiting looks just like a giant <u>bowl</u>. I'd like to take a <u>photo</u> but just looking over the edge is enough to <u>frighten</u> this <u>bright</u>-eyed reporter out of

six years' <u>growth</u>! Oh-oh! A large machine is about to <u>unload</u> a <u>piece</u> of marble that looks like a huge slab of <u>toast</u>—and I'm standing right in the way! It will be a <u>relief</u> when this assignment is over. In the meantime, I'd better take a <u>slight</u> step back and...OOOOH! This is Alexander Douglas hanging in for Kids' Report!

Observing Patterns

1. Write the list words that have two syllables. Put an accent (´) on the syllable that is stressed.

2. Write the two list words that rhyme with each word below.

       boast   delight

3. Complete these analogies with list words.
   a) **dim** is to **bright** as **closing** is to _____
   b) **juice** is to **glass** as **cereal** is to _____
   c) **asphalt** is to **driveway** as **cement** is to _____

4. Write the list word that would be found in the dictionary between these guide words.

picnic / pizza   front / gutter

Discovering Patterns

believe toast heavy below piece
bowl coast marble unload ocean
relief growth slight photo
bright opening frighten patio

1. Write the list words that have the long **e** sound /ē/ as in **chief**. Circle the letters that spell the sound /ē/ in each word.

2. Write the list words that have the long **i** sound /ī/ as in **night**. Circle the letters that spell the sound /ī/ in each word.

3. a) Ten of the list words contain the long **o** sound /ō/ as in **so**, **tow**, or **boat**.

Make a chart in your notebook like the one below. Sort the list words with the sound /ō/ into the correct categories.

/ō/ spelled **oa**	/ō/ spelled **ow**	/ō/ spelled **o**

b) Add two more words to each column which fit the patterns.

POWERBOOSTER

- The long vowel sound /ē/ is sometimes spelled **ie** as in **chief**, or **i** as in **piano**.
- The long vowel sound /ī/ is sometimes spelled **igh** as in **high**.
- The long vowel sound /ō/ may be spelled **oa** as in **boat**, **ow** as in **tow**, or **o** as in **so**.

Exploring Patterns

1. Form these letters into words with the sound /ō/ spelled **oa** or **ow**.

t   st   sn   n   sl   b   l   gr   thr   ly   ing

These list words are homographs. Use a dictionary to check their different meanings.

2. Some of the list words have different meanings depending upon how they are used in a sentence. Write the list words which complete each pair of sentences. For each sentence, write a short definition of what the word means.

a) The candies should be put in that _____ .
I like to _____ on Wednesday night.

b) Would you care for jam on your _____ ?
Let us _____ the bride and groom.

c) There are many fishing villages along the _____ .
It's fun to _____ down the hill on our toboggans.

3. **a)** Complete the word pole with words containing the sound /ī/ spelled **igh**. Use the clues to help you.

_	igh	_	ability to see
_	igh	_	perhaps, maybe
_	igh	_	disagree, engage in combat
_	igh	_	correct
_	igh	_	opposite of dark
_	igh	_	from sunset to sunrise
_	igh	_	not loose

b) Create new words with each answer above by adding word endings or making compound words.

Example: *light—sunlight*   *tight—tightly*

4. When speaking, we often use **idioms** or slang to express ideas. Rewrite each expression below so that it could be understood by someone new to the English language.

a) That test was a piece of cake!
b) The traffic was heavy.
c) You frightened the wits out of me!
d) Life is just a bowl of cherries.
e) Have you lost your marbles?

18

5. Many famous statues were sculpted from marble thousands of years ago. Some, like the famous Venus de Milo, are missing arms or a head. How do you imagine this could have happened? Write a newspaper ad for the 'Lost and Found' column of your local newspaper for the missing arms, legs, or head of a famous sculpture.

> Lost, two marble arms. Last seen attached to statue of _____ in the art museum in _____ . Generous reward of _____ is offered for any information leading to their recovery. Call 700 – 5000.

6. Write an advertisement for something you've lost. Work with a partner, editing each other's ads. How can you communicate the important information in as few words as possible?

Challenges with Words

1. Use a Super Word to replace its synonym in the paragraph below.

Inuit artists make <u>wonderful</u> carvings of animals, birds, and people out of <u>rock</u>. A sculptor can look at a piece of stone and <u>momentarily</u> catch a glimpse of the shape within. Then it takes many patient hours of labour before the shape can be <u>encouraged</u> to emerge. Inuit <u>carving</u> is internationally famous.

2. Think of three more synonyms for the Super Word **delightful**.

3. Write the base words of the four Super Words that have endings. Then write an **antonym** for each base word.

**soapstone
sculpture
borrowed
delightful
briefly
coaxed**

Antonyms are words with opposite meanings.

━━━━━ WORDS IN HISTORY ━━━━━

It is believed that **coax** comes from the English word <u>cox</u> meaning 'fool', and the French word <u>cocasse</u>, 'ridiculous'.

4. Many words in English have the long **o** sound spelled **oa** or **ow**. Use these letters to help complete the words in the story below.

Winsl _ _ 's eyes were agl _ _ with pleasure as he appr _ _ ched the bungal _ _ on the seac _ _ st. It was a sh _ _ piece of design. Each wind _ _ was framed in white. Inside, the floors were mell _ _ _ _ k and the washb _ _ ls were marble. "It's all mine!" he b _ _ sted, his voice hoarse with pride, a lump in his thr _ _ t. Then a furr _ _ of dismay creased his forehead. At his elb _ _ was a new lawn m _ _ er, ready to cut the hectare of green grass. "And this is mine too," he said sorr _ _ fully.

5. Rocking Research: Use encyclopedias, reference books, magazines, or a CD-ROM on a computer to find information about three types of rocks. Organize your information in a chart such as the one below.

Type of rock	Limestone	Marble	Soapstone
Appearance Where found Uses			

6. Is it Art? When this statue was put up at City Hall, some people loved it , some hated it. Write a review, telling what you think of the sculpture. Support your opinion.

Proofread your writing with a partner.

5

Long u
ui u_e oo ew
jui**c**y **ch**u**t**e **f**oo**l**e**d kn**e**w**

suitable
fooled
edit
cartoon
nuisance
shoot
choose
convert
juicy
groove
chute
type
consumer
digital
conclude
threw
flute
knew

Lead into Light

Today's report on what's new in the <u>digital</u> computer world concerns desktop publishing. Did you know that you can write, <u>edit</u>, and publish a <u>cartoon</u> book, or a <u>juicy</u> adventure story right in your own home? Just <u>choose</u> a laser printer that is <u>suitable</u> for your needs and go to it. Don't be <u>fooled</u> by the printer's small size—it can <u>convert</u> electrical impulses from your computer into tiny dots on a sheet of paper.

The average <u>consumer</u> will need a laser that prints 300 dots per 2.5 centimetres. If you <u>conclude</u> that you want to be a pro, you can buy laser printers that will <u>shoot</u> over 2000 dots per 2.5 centimetres! Perhaps you thought that the sound of your old printer was a <u>nuisance</u>.

Maybe your parents thought it was louder than the sound you made when you practised the <u>flute</u>. But, don't worry. Laser printers are entirely silent.

Twenty years ago, no one <u>knew</u> that computers would replace printing presses. Old-fashioned <u>type</u> was made when molten lead poured down a <u>chute</u> into molds. The lead filled each tiny <u>groove</u> to make perfect letters. It may have been more perfect, but it was certainly slower. This is Beverley Windsor for Kids' Report, signing off with my laser printer.

Observing Patterns

1. Write the list words that are similar in meaning to the words below.

select	finish	customer	transform
pest	proper	tricked	comics

2. a) Write the two list words which are **homophones** for one another.

b) Write two other list words which have homophones.

3. Write the list words that match these shapes.

| | | | | | | | | | | | | | | | | | |

4. Supply the missing letters for these list words.

    a) cart _ _ n
    b) s _ _ t _ ble
    c) dig _ t _ l
    d) gr _ _ ve
    e) n _ _ s _ nce
    f) _ _ ute

Discovering Patterns

suitable fooled edit cartoon
nuisance shoot choose convert
juicy groove chute type consumer
digital conclude threw flute knew

1. Many of the list words contain the long **u** sound as in **fruit**, **boot**, **conclude**, and **threw**. Some of the long **u** list words can be pronounced two ways. For example, the long **u** sound in **nuisance**, **costume**, and **new** can be pronounced /ü/ or /yü/.

Sort the words with the long **u** sound into the correct categories.

/ü/ and/or /yü/			
spelled **ui**	spelled **u-consonant-e**	spelled **oo**	spelled **ew**

POWERBOOSTER

- The long vowel sound /ü/ is sometimes spelled **ui** as in **fruit**, **u-consonant-e** as in **conclude**, **oo** as in **boot**, or **ew** as in **threw**.
- The vowel sounds /yü/ and /ü/ are sometimes spelled **ui** as in **nuisance**, **u-consonant-e** as in **costume**, and **ew** as in **new**.

Exploring Patterns

1. Complete the word pole with words that end in **oon** as in **cartoon**. Use the picture clues to help you. You might want to check the spelling of the words in a dictionary.

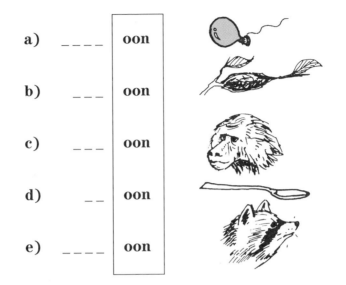

a)	_ _ _ _	**oon**
b)	_ _ _	**oon**
c)	_ _ _	**oon**
d)	_ _	**oon**
e)	_ _ _ _	**oon**

2. The list words **edit** and **convert** are base words for a number of different forms that share a similar meaning with the base. Rewrite each sentence below using the correct form of the words.

a) The _____ of the local newspaper wrote an _____ about the new highway.

editorial   editor

b) The _____ to metric units took place in the 1970s in Canada.

We used our _____ to turn on the television.

A _____ is a car with a removable roof.

converter   convertible   conversion

3. An **acronym** is a word made up of the first letter of other words. For example, **laser** is an acronym for **l**ight **a**mplification by **s**timulated **e**mission of **r**adiation.

Some acronyms are written with capital letters, others are written in lowercase letters. To be sure of the spelling check a dictionary.

a) Write the acronyms for the following:
North Atlantic Treaty Organization
United Nations International Children's Emergency Fund

b) Use a dictionary or your own knowledge to explain the full meaning of the following acronyms.

sonar   scuba   FYI

4. Proofread this news item, looking for homophone errors. Rewrite the passage correctly.

My father bought a knew kitchen gadget called a Coleslaw Shooter. I new we were in trouble when it started to chute shredded cabbage all over the kitchen. It through cabbage all over the floor! "Can't you stop it?" I yelled.

"It doesn't have a break" my father said. "We'll just have to weight until it's threw shredding."

5. What would you like to publish? A 'buy and sell' newsletter for kids in your neighbourhood? An engraved invitation to your next party? Posters for a local event? Choose a publishing project and design a poster, invitation, or advertisement. Perhaps you could desktop publish it electronically on your school computer.

Challenges with Words

1. Write the Super Words that mean almost the same as the underlined words or phrases.

This is my <u>chance</u> to get a great story for our weekly <u>journal</u>! I've just seen the famous movie star, Zena Katrina, leaving the <u>workshop</u> of her movie company. I'd like to interview her about the <u>argument</u> she's having with the company concerning her next movie. If I'm successful in my <u>chase</u> of this story, it will be a great article. I'll just have to remember to <u>check it word by word</u> before I submit it.

━━━ **WORDS IN HISTORY** ━━━

Studio comes from the Italian <u>studio</u>, 'a place for painters', originally from the Latin **stadium**, 'a place of study'.

2. a) We often use 'warm' words to describe objects or situations. Rank the following adjectives from coolest to hottest. You might compare your rankings with a partner and discuss any differences.

sizzling lukewarm feverish cozy hot

b) Match each of the adjectives above with Super Words. Then write sentences containing the word pairs that you chose.

Example: *The reporter was in <u>hot pursuit</u> of a story.*

3. Think of five 'cold' adjectives, and rank them in order of coolness.

4. An important step in writing is **proofreading**. Interview a classmate about his or her proofreading habits. You might want to ask questions such as: Do you proofread by yourself or with a partner? What marks do you use in proofreading? How long does it usually take? Why is proofreading important?

Use the answers your classmate provides to write a report about proofreading. Then trade reports and proofread each other's work. If you always use the same proofreaders' marks, it is easier for others to correct errors.

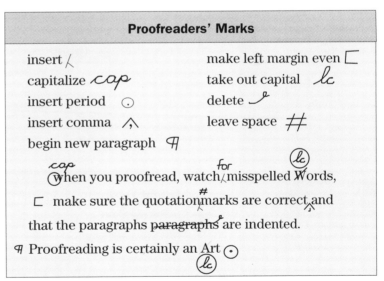

5. New acronyms are created all the time. They are made up of the first letters of other words and are often spelled with capital letters. Match the acronyms in the new word list with their correct meanings below.

a) Self-Adressed Stamped Envelope
b) As Soon As Possible
c) Thank Goodness It's Friday

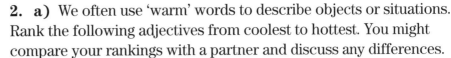

TGIF
SASE
ASAP

25

6 Looking Back

STUDY STEPS

LOOK at each word.

SAY each word.

COVER each word.

WRITE each word.

CHECK each word carefully.

Here is a list of challenging words from Units 1–5.

except	nuisance	believe	escape
knew	hurry	frighten	weigh
proceed	freight	only	bury
really	nectar	whole	threw
sleigh	ocean	bomb	chute

1. Use the Study Steps for each word. Your teacher will then dictate the words.

2. Complete this story with words from the Study List.

Yesterday I was in a _____ to get to school. I _____ I was riding my bike too fast, but I _____ wanted to be on time for soccer practice. Even though the light was red, I started to _____ through the intersection. Suddenly, it was like a _____ had gone off! A car hit my bike and _____ me to the sidewalk. My _____ bike was wrecked _____ for one wheel. I don't _____ easily, but _____ me, I was scared! Even though walking to school is a _____, I was lucky to _____ without serious injuries.

3. Correct any spelling errors in the following signs. Pay special attention to **homophones**.

a) (sign at a health club)

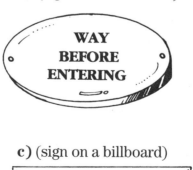

WAY BEFORE ENTERING

b) (sign at a campsite)

BERRY YOUR GARBAGE

c) (sign on a billboard)

CONGRATULATIONS! WE NEW YOU COULD DO IT!

d) (sign at a winter carnival)

SLAY RIDES FOR THE HOLE FAMILY

4. Complete the sentences with words containing the long **u** sound /ü/ as in **fruit**, **moon**, **threw**, or **rule**, or /yü/ as in **dispute** or **ewe**.

All the syllables you will use are in the box below.

con	con	con	co	com	car	cur	clude	cash
few	sum	toon	fuse	coon	put	ew	er	er

a) c _ _ _ _ _ _ mix up; mistake one thing for another

b) c _ _ _ _ _ covering prepared by the larvae of many kinds of insects

c) c _ _ _ _ _ _ _ person who buys and uses food, clothing, etc.

d) c _ _ _ _ _ _ humorous drawing

e) c _ _ _ _ _ the time you must be home at night

f) c _ _ _ _ _ _ _ a machine that can store and process data

g) c _ _ _ _ _ a small, edible, kidney-shaped nut

h) c _ _ _ _ _ _ _ to end, finish

5. Complete this chart with words that fit the meaning category and contain the long vowel sound needed. An example is given for each row.

	a	e	i	o
Food				oatmeal
Names of people			Irene	
Sports		field hockey		
Animals	snake			

27

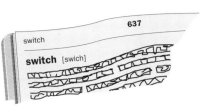

Dictionary Skills

1. Entry Words: Most entry words in a dictionary have more than one meaning. The different meanings help us to understand the word better and how it can be used in other ways.

Read the entry for the word **switch**.

> **switch** (swich) **1** a device for making or breaking a connection in an electric circuit. **2** turn aside; change course or direction. **3** exchange. **4** a stroke; lash.

You will often find an illustrative sentence, printed in italic type, following the definition of an entry word.

Read these illustrative sentences for **switch** and match them with the number of the entry definition.

> **a)** *They switched jackets.*
> **b)** *The dog broke a vase with a switch of its tail.*
> **c)** *We could not find the light switch in the dark room.*
> **d)** *He was driving on the outside lane but suddenly switched.*

2. Read the entry for the word **lock**.

> **lock** (lok) **1** a means of fastening doors, boxes, etc. usually needing a key of special shape to open it. **2** fasten with a lock. **3** an enclosed section of a canal, dock, etc., in which the level of the water can be changed by letting the water in or out, to raise or lower ships. **4** join, fit, or link together. **5** in wrestling, a kind of hold.

Write an illustrative sentence for each of the definitions of **lock**.

3. Use a dictionary to find at least four definitions for the word **stage**. Beside each definition write an illustrative sentence.

Just the Facts

1. A good newspaper story answers the five Ws in its opening paragraph: **WHO? WHAT? WHERE? WHEN? WHY?**

    a) Write down the name of an event at home, at school, or in your community.

    b) Now, brainstorm a list of all the details which describe the event.

    c) Classify your list of details under the five Ws.

2. Imagine you are a newspaper reporter with a deadline to meet. Write a newspaper article about the event you chose above. Try to answer the five Ws in your first paragraph.

3. Have a partner proofread your story before it goes to press.

Grammar Power

1. Sentence Fragments: When we talk, we often use bits of sentences. For example: "Over there", "When I get time", and "We used to". Nobody minds these fragments in speech, but in written work, they can leave the reader hanging.

Finish these sentence fragments below.

a) When I get home from school _____ because I'm so hungry.

b) The big, beautiful peanut butter sandwich _____ .

c) The TV in the living room _____ .

2. Are they sentences or fragments? Write each group of words below. If it is a complete sentence, add a capital at the beginning and a period at the end.

a) sometimes the best ideas

b) everybody has good ideas

c) when I had that brillant brain wave

d) learn how to put your ideas into action

3. Subject and Object Pronouns: Look at the pronouns below.

Subject Pronouns	Object Pronouns
I	me
you	you
she	her
he	him
we	us
they	them
it	it

Pronouns such as **I** and **she** are used as the subject of the sentence. **I** and **she** are what the sentence is about.

Example: *I am drinking milk.*   *She is singing a song.*

Pronouns such as **me** and **her** are object pronouns. They tell **who** or **what** is the object of the action in the sentence.

Example: *Give the milk to **me**.*   *She is singing that song to **her**.*

"Who's there?" "It's me," not "It's I" answers this question. We often use different pronouns in speaking than in writing.

4. Choose a pronoun that fits each blank. If you have two subjects, like **she** and **I**, you have to use two subject pronouns. For example, Her and I...(wrong)   She and I...(right).

(*She*, *her*) is my best friend. I phone (*she*, *her*) every night after dinner. My parents wonder how (*she*, *her*) and I have so much to say to each other, but (*I*, *me*) tell (*she*, *her*) everything important that happens to (*me*, *I*).

Proofing Power

Proofread the passage below, then rewrite it correcting all the spelling errors that you find.

Journalists often use a form of organizing information called 'dot-jot'. They include nothing exept the facts when they do this. Here is an example:

frieght train story

- freight train derailed
- spilled grape necter drink everywhere
- through a hole shipment of the drink onto tracks
- an oceon of the drink covered trackes
- people reely has to hurray if they wanted some
- train will procede when back on tracks
- will way much less without the liquid

That's how reporters record their facts! Beleave me, it was a nuisance to clean up. If onely I had been there! I love grape nector!

R-controlled Vowels

or our ore ar

orbit **s**ource ign**ore** **ch**art

orbit
department
sparkling
target
source
explore
formula
giant
hardly
chart
important
yourself
ignore
transform
absorb
forward
dwarf
fourth

Red Giant into White Dwarf

Hello, this is Nigel DeBarlo. I'm interviewing Dr. Anna Astro at the <u>Department</u> of Astronomy. Dr. Astro, let's <u>explore</u> the world beyond our solar system.

DR. A: Fine, Nigel. Our <u>target</u> on the star <u>chart</u> is this red <u>giant</u> star. It's gradually cooling. If you could send <u>yourself</u> <u>forward</u> in time you could watch it <u>transform</u> into a white <u>dwarf</u>, the <u>fourth</u> largest type of star.

NIGEL: This is fascinating. I hope I can <u>absorb</u> all this information.

DR. A: Well, you can <u>ignore</u> some of the scientific terms. What's <u>important</u> is that stars <u>hardly</u> ever stay the same. They're always changing.

NIGEL: What's the <u>formula</u> that makes the stars shine, Doctor?

DR. A: Well, Nigel, the <u>source</u> of a star's <u>sparkling</u> light is hydrogen. Most stars have enough hydrogen to burn for billions of years! That's good news for planets like Earth, which <u>orbit</u> around a star.

NIGEL: Thanks, Dr. Astro. Stargazing looks like a lot of fun.

Observing Patterns

1. **a)** Write the two-syllable list words in two columns. Place an accent (´) on the stressed syllable.

First syllable stressed as in **plánet**	Second syllable stressed as in **infórm**

b) Write the three list words that have three syllables. Place an accent (´) on the stressed syllable.

2. Complete each set with a list word.

  a) vital, significant, crucial, _____
  b) archery, darts, bull's eye, _____
  c) diagram, map, graph, _____
  d) first, second, third, _____
  e) mixture, recipe, composition, _____
  f) beginning, base, origin, _____

3. Write the list words that match these shapes.

|‖‖| ‖|‖‖| ‖‖‖|

Discovering Patterns

orbit department sparkling target source explore formula giant hardly chart important yourself ignore transform absorb forward dwarf fourth

1. a) Many of the list words contain the r-controlled /ôr/ as in **more**. This sound can be spelled in a number of ways. Draw the chart below and sort the list words with the /ôr/ sound into the correct categories.

spelled **or** as in **born**	spelled **our** as in **pour**	spelled **ore** as in **more**	spelled **ar** as in **war**

  b) Add two other words that you know to each column.

2. a) Other list words contain the sound /är/ as in **dark**. Write the list words which spell the sound /är/. Circle the letters which spell the sound /är/.
  b) Write two other words that you know which contain the sound /är/.

POWERBOOSTER

- The sound /ôr/ may be spelled a number of ways, including **or**, **our**, **ore**, and **ar**.
- The sound /är/ is usually spelled **ar**.

Exploring Patterns

1. Combine the words on the stars to make six two-syllable words with the sound /ôr/.

2. The prefix **trans-** comes from Latin and has more than one meaning. In the word **transform**, **trans-** means 'into a different place or condition'.

a) Select the correct word derived from **transform** to complete each sentence. Notice that each word means 'into a different place or condition'.

transformer   transformed   transformation

The decorating committee _____ the gymnasium into a fabulous carnival.

The make-up artist's _____ of the girl into a woman was amazing.

A _____ was needed to step-down the voltage for consumer use.

b) The prefix **trans-** may also mean 'across', 'over', or 'through'. Your dictionary contains dozens of words which have this prefix. Choose four of them and write your own sentences.

3. Design word webs for the list words below. You may use any word that is connected in some way to the centre word.

orbit   explore   yourself

Example:

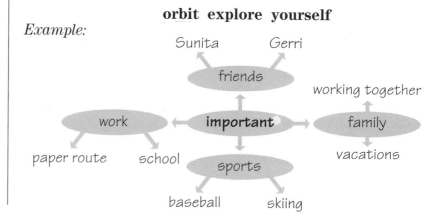

Hint! Word webs are fun to make with a partner or in a small group.

32

4. The use of list words and phrases in the following sentences may be difficult to understand. Rewrite each sentence so that the meaning is clear.

a) Her criticism of the movie was <u>right on target</u>.

b) The newspaper reporter refused to <u>reveal her source</u>.

c) My brother was <u>absorbed</u> for many hours in solving the jigsaw puzzle.

5. **What would you take?** Suppose that space travel is possible, and you are journeying to a distant star. You can take only six of your favourite possessions. List the six you would choose, and explain why you can't leave Earth without them!

6. In the eyepiece of the telescope you glimpse a new comet. As its discoverer, you are given the chance to name it. What name will you choose, and why?

Challenges with Words

1. Write the Super Word that fits each set of words below.

a) Pleides, Leo, Virgo, _____

b) geographers, paleontologists, biologists, _____

c) group, collection, system, _____

d) sonar, microwave, radio, _____

e) sorrowful, gloomy, depressing, _____

f) comet, asteroid, planet, _____

SUPER WORDS

meteor
radar
astronomers
mournful
constellation
Orion

━━━━━━━━ **WORDS IN HISTORY** ━━━━━━━━

The Greek word <u>astron</u> means 'star'. Many English words begin with **astro** and have something to do with the stars.

2. **a)** Check your dictionary for words that begin with **astro**. Choose three and rewrite their definitions in your own words.

b) Make up three **astro** words of your own, and use them in sentences.

*Example: I landed my space ship at the **astroport**.*

3. Think of six words associated with stars. Write them in a list. Then write an antonym, or opposite, for each word.

Example: bright dim

4. The Super Word **radar** is an **acronym** made from the first letters of **RA**dio **D**etecting **A**nd **R**anging. What do these acronyms stand for? Guess as many as you can. Then check your answers in a dictionary or reference book.

    a) COD   **b)** ICBM
    c) RV   **d)** CBC
    e) ATV   **f)** VIP

5. Imagine that you are looking through the telescope one night when you see a large object hurtling toward Earth's atmosphere. Fill in the blanks below using Super Words. Then finish the story in your own words.

My voice was tense with worry as I spoke to the _____ at the observatory. "I've picked up a massive object, on the _____ screen," I snapped. "It's coming from the direction of the _____ ."

The _____ voice of my boss replied, "It's likely just a _____ . It will burn up before it ever reaches Earth's surface."

But I knew....

6. New kinds of fruits and vegetables are always being developed. Match the new words with the clues below.

    a) a combination of broccoli and cauliflower
    b) a combination of a tangerine and an orange
    c) a combination of cauliflower, broccoli, and cabbage

NEW WORDS

tangelos

broccoflower

romanesco

8

R-controlled Vowels
er ir ur ear
al**er**t d**ir**ty **ur**gent h**ear**d

fertile
birth
urgent
canals
burning
dirty
heard*
necessary
conserve
irrigate
alert
expert
certainly
patterns
surprise
blurred
swirls
burden

Sand to Strawberries

Hello, everyone. This is Amy Wong, in the New Mexican desert. I'm about to witness the birth of a strawberry field.

It may come as a surprise to you that not all deserts are places where the sand swirls around you, your vision is blurred by dust, and sand dunes in strange patterns spread across the landscape. Here in New Mexico, a truck is more likely to carry your burden than a camel! The water trickling through these canals at my feet may look dirty, but every drop is necessary to irrigate this dry, but fertile, desert soil. Next year, with the expert use of irrigation, a crop of luscious strawberries will grow on this spot. But in this desert, just as in the Sahara, people must certainly be alert to conserve the green fields.

We've all heard of the famines in Africa. There, deserts like the Sahara are growing. Overgrazing by cattle and the burning of brush on the edge of desert lands have caused an urgent problem.

This is Amy Wong for Kids' Report. I think I'll go and get a drink of water!

Observing Patterns

1. Write the list words that mean the **opposite** of the following.
   a) drowsy _____
   b) arid _____
   c) death _____
   d) clear, in focus _____
   e) waste _____
   f) clean _____
   g) beginner _____

2. Write the list words that fit these clues.
   a) two words in which the sound /s/ is spelled **c**
   b) four words in which the sound /z/ is spelled **s**
   c) four words that contain a **double consonant**
   d) a word in which the sound /j/ is spelled **g**

*Heard is a frequently misspelled word.

35

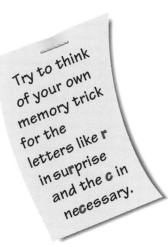

Try to think of your own memory trick for the letters like **r** in **surprise** and the **c** in **necessary**.

3. Write in alphabetical order, the list words that would be found between these words in a dictionary.

   a) after / burp
   a _ _ _ ◯ ,   b _ ◯ _ _ ,   b _ _ _ _ ◯ _ ,
   b _ _ _ ◯ _ ,   b _ ◯ _ _ _ _

   b) cage / early:
   c _ _ _ _ ◯ ,   c ◯ _ ◯ _ _ _ _ _ ,   c ◯ _ _ _ _ _ _ ,
   d _ _ ◯ _

   c) earnest / hurry
   e _ _ _ _ ◯ ,   f _ _ ◯ _ _ _ ,   h ◯ _ _ _

Unscramble the circled letters to answer this riddle: How can a small child lift an adult in the air?

On _ _ _ _ _ _ _ _ _ _ _ _ _

Discovering Patterns

fertile birth urgent canals burning dirty heard necessary conserve irrigate alert expert certainly patterns surprise blurred swirls burden

1. **a)** Many of the list words have the r-controlled /ėr/ as in **bird**. Notice the letters which spell the /ėr/ sound in each word. Sort the list words with the sound /ėr/ into the following categories.

spelled **er** as in **person**	spelled **ir** as in **bird**	spelled **ur** as in **churn**	spelled **ear** as in **earn**

   b) Add two other words which fit the patterns to each column.

POWERBOOSTER

- The sound /ėr/ may be spelled in a number of ways, including **er**, **ir**, **ur**, and **ear**.

Exploring Patterns

1. Write the list words that complete this paragraph.

If you fly over Holland, it will be a _ _ _ _ _ _ _ _ to see neat patchwork _ _ _ _ _ _ _ _ of fields. The Dutch people are _ _ _ _ _ _ <u>s</u> at conserving water to keep their land _ _ _ _ _ _ _. They have found it _ _ _ _ _ _ _ _ _ to build a system of _ _ _ _ _ _ to control water and _ _ _ _ _ _ _ _ the land. The green fields _ _ _ _ _ _ _ _ _ show how successful their efforts have been.

2. Solve this puzzle using the clues provided. Then unscramble the letters to describe a problem which threatens Canada's farmlands.

    a) This letter is in **purpose** but not in **surprise** _

    b) This letter is in **pearl** but not in **permanent** _

    c) This letter is in **burn** but not in **born** _

    d) This letter is in **pattern** but not in **trainer** _

    e) This letter is in **alert** but not in **learn** _

    f) This letter is in **earn** but not in **heard** _

    g) This letter is in **broker** but not in **beaker** _

    h) This letter is in **dirty** but not in **yesterday** _

    i) This letter is in **early** but not in **yearn** _

The fertility of Canada's farmlands is threatened by _ _ _ _ _ _ _ _ _.

3. The following nouns are each related to a list word:

irrigation   conservation   urgency

    a) Write the words. Beside each, write the list word to which it is related. How were each of the words changed to form nouns?
    b) Write sentences using these nouns.

4. Complete the following definitions with /ėr/ words related to **farming**. Read the clues carefully.

Example: *sometimes made from manure to add nutrients to the soil*

    <u>f e r t i l i z e r</u>

    a) found on surface of soil after rain; a delicacy for birds!
    _ _ r _ _ w _ _ _ _
    b) a fowl popular at Thanksgiving _ _ r _ _ _
    c) farmers must start their work very _ _ r _ _ in the morning
    d) a group of goats or horses _ _ r _

What other verbs do you add -tion to, to make nouns? Try *erupt, contract,* and *subtract.*

37

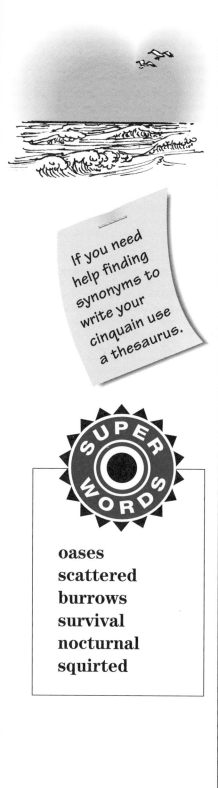

5. **a)** A **cinquain** is a five-line poem. You build a cinquain like this:

First line: a name for something
Second line: two words to describe it
Third line: three words that tell what it does
Fourth line: a clear picture using 'as _____ as'
Fifth line: another name for it

Here is an example of a cinquain about the ocean.

Ocean
Shimmering, deep,
Swells, tumbles, thunders,
As dark as great storm clouds.
Endless.

Write a cinquain about the desert or another natural setting. When you have finished, see if you can substitute more vivid words for some you have written. Share your poem with a partner.

Challenges with Words

1. Correct the passage below by writing the Super Words that are the **antonyms** of the underlined words or phrases.

Although the desert may seem barren and lifeless, it is actually full of life. Many desert animals are <u>out during the day</u>. They come out when the desert is at its coolest. Their <u>destruction</u> depends on staying deep in their <u>mounds</u> during the hottest part of the day.

Desert plants survive by storing water in their fleshy stems and leaves. You may be <u>spattered</u> with water if you break the leaf of a cactus plant.

People live in the desert too. <u>Crowded</u> across its surface are small <u>dry spots</u> where underground springs provide the water supply for small settlements.

2. Strange Plurals! Some words, such as the Super Word **oases**, make the plural form by changing **-is** at the end of a word to **-es**. Correct this sentence, using the singular form of the underlined words.

It's a <u>crises</u> when drought threatens an <u>oases</u>, which is the <u>bases</u> of desert life.

If you need help finding synonyms to write your cinquain use a thesaurus.

SUPER WORDS

oases
scattered
burrows
survival
nocturnal
squirted

38

3. Complete these analogies, then compare your responses with a partner's.

  a) **wet** is to **dry** as **ocean** is to _____
  b) **water** is to **oases** as **sand** is to _____
  c) **tent** is to **desert** as **cabin** is to _____
  d) **camel** is to **desert** as **ship** is to _____

4. **a)** **Desert Search:** Use the clues to help you solve this word puzzle. Each word in your answer will overlap with the next word.

  • mounds of loose sand (5 letters)
  • name of African desert (6 letters)
  • plant with spines and no leaves (6 letters)
  • a fertile place (5 letters)
  • a desert wanderer (5 letters)
  • a barren land (6 letters)

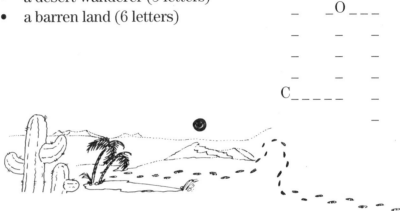

b) Think of other words related to the word **desert**. Create a similar puzzle using your words and try it on a partner.

5. **Water, water everywhere!** Brainstorm to find words that describe how water comes out of a tap. Then rank the words from **dripped** to **gushed**. Don't forget the Super Word **squirted**!

6. Create a bumper sticker to remind people how important it is to save water.

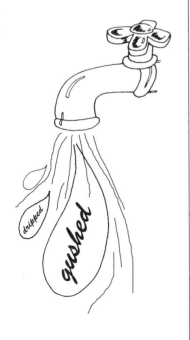

Other Vowels

oi oy ou ow

moist annoyed foul drowned

annoyed
drowned
moist
join
towering
employed
avoid
powerful
poison
doubt
choice
different
wicked
changed
foul
crouch
stories
enjoyable

Movie FX

This is Alexander Douglas for Kids' Report. Join us on the set of a new movie, *The Dragonfly*. Action movies may not be your favourite choice, but here at Flicks Inc., dozens of people are employed to turn actor J.J. Duncan into a powerful, winged monster. There is no doubt J.J. will be different when they are through. He will be changed by the magic of special effects, or FX as they are called in motion picture language.

This is one of the most exciting stories I've ever heard. I'm sure the movie will be most enjoyable. J.J. will crouch inside his costume and turn into that foul fiend, the Dragonfly. The wicked Dragonfly manages to avoid all the traps set for it, including the poison in its sugar water. Towering above us here on the set, is the bridge from which the 'fly' leaps at the end of the movie. I'm sure every eye will be moist when the Dragonfly is drowned. Oops! I think I just gave away the end of the movie. I hope you're not too annoyed.

Observing Patterns

1. Write the base words for these list words.

   enjoyable employed annoyed towering
   drowned powerful stories changed

2. Write the list words that fit the clues below.
   a) three syllables, with the stress on the first syllable
   b) four syllables, with the stress on the second syllable
   c) contains the sound /ch/
   d) the letter **b** does not make the /b/ sound
   e) the sound /z/ in the middle of a word is spelled **s**

3. Write the list words that rhyme with the words below.
   hoist coin howl

4. **a)** Complete the following sets with list words.

evil, scheming, mean, _____
run away, hide, miss, _____
damp, wet, watery, _____

b) Create two more sets that can be completed by list words. Try them out on a partner.

Discovering Patterns

annoyed drowned moist join towering employed avoid powerful poison doubt choice different wicked changed foul crouch stories enjoyable

1. Many of the list words contain the sound /ou/ as in **mountain** or **flower**.

Sort the words with the /ou/ sound into two categories.

/ou/ spelled **ou** as in **mountain**	/ou/ spelled **ow** as in **flower**

2. Other list words contain the sound /oi/ as in **noise** or **joy**. Complete the chart with list words which have the /oi/ sound. How is the /oi/ sound spelled in these words?

/oi/ spelled **oi** as in **noise**	/oi/ spelled **oy** as in **joy**

POWERBOOSTER

- The sound /ou/ is sometimes spelled **ou** as in **doubt** or **ow** as in **down**.
- The sound /oi/ may be spelled **oi** as in **join** or **oy** as in **enjoy**.

Can you find other words that fit these patterns?

Exploring Patterns

1. Complete this story with words from the box. Each answer will contain the /oi/ sound.

enjoyable	choice	noise	voice
toy	pointed	noisy	disappointed
destroyed	coin	boiling	

I gave my little sister the _____ of going to a quiet movie or a _____ amusement park. Naturally, she chose the park! I could scarcely hear my own _____ over all the _____ . Every time she _____ to a ride, I would have to give another _____ to the ticket seller. She won a small _____ at the dart game, but was _____ that she didn't win a huge stuffed animal. The sun was _____ hot and I _____ my new shoes in the dirt, but for my sister, it was the most _____ day of the summer!

2. From each set of words below, write the <u>two</u> words that have the sound /ou/ as in **doubt** or **powerful**.

    a) bought   drowned   house   known
    b) foul   enough   blowing   growl
    c) would   crouch   flown   frown
    d) thought   grown   ground   towering

3. Word Explosions: Explode these base words in your 'word laboratory' to create new forms of the words.

employ enjoy

Example:

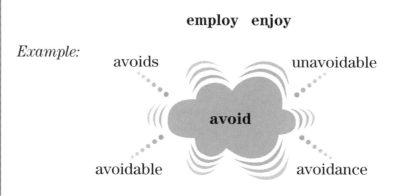

42

4. Many of the list words have endings added to the base word. Add the endings on the filmstrip to the base words on the film cans to make list words. Write these as a formula.

Example: change + -ed = changed

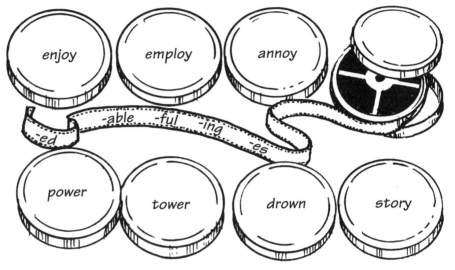

5. If the Dragonfly in the movie has not really drowned, you can be sure there will be a *Dragonfly II*. Write a brief outline of what you think the plot might be. Try to fit the whole story into fifty words or less.

6. Make a poster, or advertisement for *Dragonfly II*.

Challenges with Words

1. Rewrite the sentences, using Super Words in place of the underlined words or phrases.

    a) The director knew she could count on the <u>faithfulness</u> of her actors.

    b) He had one <u>scheduled meeting</u> at the movie studio.

    c) We will <u>refuse to buy or use</u> that soap, because the people who make it are on strike.

    d) Jake, don't <u>draw your eyebrows together or tighten your mouth</u> when you say your lines!

    e) That <u>artificial bird</u> looks very real on stage.

    f) She helped build the <u>base</u> of the movie set.

2. Multiple Meanings: Use your dictionary to write three meanings for each of the following Super Words. Then write a sentence using each word to show one of its meanings.

foundation   decoy   appointment

SUPER WORDS

appointment
foundation
decoy
loyalty
boycott
scowl

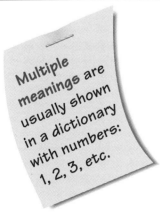
Multiple meanings are usually shown in a dictionary with numbers: 1, 2, 3, etc.

3. Actors are able to express a wide range of feelings. The Super Word **scowl** is a word which describes how a person looks and feels. Unscramble the words in the box and match the words to the clues below. Each word describes a feeling.

nfrwo	clkehuc	nwki
wnay	rlage	lmise

   a) something you do when tired, or bored   _ _ _ _
   b) to laugh quietly   _ _ _ _ _ _ _
   c) an upward curve of the mouth   _ _ _ _ _
   d) a fierce, angry stare   _ _ _ _ _
   e) to close and open one eye quickly   _ _ _ _
   f) to draw the brows together   _ _ _ _ _

4. The /**oi**/ sound is spelled in different ways. Find words that contain this sound to complete the sentences below. A spelling clue is given for each one.

   a) The _ _ _loi_ steak looked a bit oi_ _ and greasy when it slid out of the _ _oil _ _ .
   b) The oy_ _ _ _ _ will _ _oi_ if we don't get them out of their shells.
   c) The brave e_ _oy proved he was _oy_ _ to the _oy_ _ family.

5. Put on your movie writer's hat. Flicks Inc. has just signed you to write a sci-fi, special effects movie. Decide on an attention-grabbing title and write a description of your movie.

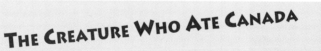

6. Television and movies are changing all the time, and adding new words to our language. Unscramble the words in the sentences below.

   a) Products shown on **lfimcrseinoa** can be ordered.
   b) That **erssn-iemii** had sixteen parts!
   c) You can watch programs on or play games on **ctreineivat VT.**

10

Compound Words

teamwork

satisfaction

teamwork

infield

success

baseball

champions

someday

shortstop

attitude

coach

scoreboard

co-operate

loudspeaker

highland

clubhouse

carefree

clipboard

outlook

Players into Champions

This is Beverley Windsor in the <u>clubhouse</u> of the <u>Highland</u> Heroes where the <u>loudspeaker</u> has just announced the final score of 6 to 4 for the Heroes. Here comes <u>Coach</u> Flynn carrying her <u>clipboard</u> and wearing her team's sweat shirt. Coach, what makes a championship team?
COACH: Well, Bev, I think <u>attitude</u> is important. In order to have <u>success</u> in <u>baseball</u> or any sport, the players need a winning <u>outlook.</u>
BEV: I suppose <u>teamwork</u> is important too.

COACH: That's right. Each player, from pitcher to <u>shortstop,</u> has to <u>co-operate</u> to win.
BEV: It must give you a lot of <u>satisfaction</u> to see the results of your hard work up there on the <u>scoreboard</u>.
COACH: That's correct. Tonight, the team is <u>carefree</u>, but tomorrow, we go right back to work. I'd like to see the Heroes as strong in the outfield, as they are in the <u>infield</u>. <u>Someday</u>, I'd like to see the team become cross-Canada <u>champions</u>!

Observing Patterns

1. **a)** Write the two list words that have four syllables.
   b) Find three list words with three syllables.

2. Write the list words that contain double consonants. Circle the double consonants in each word.

3. **a)** Five list words contain the long **e** sound. Write the words in the following order.

   /ē/ spelled **ea** (2 words)
   /ē/ spelled **ie** (1 word)
   /ē/ spelled **i** (1 word)
   /ē/ spelled **ee** (1 word)

   b) Add two more words with the /ē/ sound to each pattern.

4. Combine the words in the box to make seven list words.

stop	board	look	house	board	day	land
clip	some	high	club	score	out	short

5. Complete these analogies by using list words.
   a) **teacher** is to **students** as _____ is to **players**
   b) **stick** is to **hockey** as **bat** is to _____
   c) **fielder** is to **outfield** as **pitcher** is to _____
   d) **failure** is to **success** as **worried** is to _____

Discovering Patterns

satisfaction teamwork infield
success baseball champions someday
shortstop attitude coach scoreboard
co-operate loudspeaker highland
clubhouse carefree clipboard outlook

1. Write the list words that are formed by the joining of two smaller words. Underline the two base words in each. We call these words **compound words**. In compound words, the two base words make sense together.

*Example: The **weekend** comes at the end of the week.*

- Compound words are formed from two smaller words which have a logical connection in meaning.

Exploring Patterns

1. **a)** Examine the picture clues and follow the lines between clues to form six compound words.

b) Create other compound words containing one of the above picture clues.

Example: dishwasher

2. **Compound Puns:** Solve each riddle with a compound word from the box below.

loudspeaker	lawsuit
sunflower	carefree
quicksand	peppermint
clubhouse	crosswalk

  a) something you wear in court
  b) the hottest plant in the solar system
  c) a noisy talker
  d) runners love this sand
  e) the kind of walk you take when you're angry
  f) inexpensive help
  g) a candy that makes you sneeze
  h) where cave people stored their weapons

3. Complete the word pole with words you think are important qualities for success in sports or in school.

Example: **A S K   QUESTIONS**
                 U
                 C
                 C
                 E
                 S
                 S

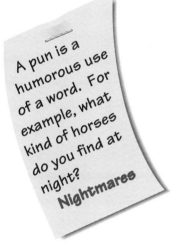

A pun is a humorous use of a word. For example, what kind of horses do you find at night? **Nightmares**

roughhouse
umpire
kneepad
scrimmage
quarterback
touchdown

4. Combine each pair of sentences to form one longer sentence.
   a) The shortstop scooped up the baseball. Then she threw it to second base.
   b) The coach said teamwork would lead to success. A positive attitude would, too.
   c) The voice on the loudspeaker said the score was tied. The scoreboard said that we were leading by a run.

5. How do you feel when you **win** or **lose** a sports game?
   a) Write **six** words you associate with winning.
   b) Write **six** words you associate with losing.
   c) Write a **two** stanza **cinquain** about winning and losing, choosing words carefully for best effect. Look back to Unit 8 to review the cinquain. Read your poem to a partner.

Challenges with Words

1. **a)** Write the Super Word that best fits each set.

   play, huddle, pass, _____
   pitcher, goalie, shortstop, _____
   referee, official, judge, _____
   goal, point, basket, _____
   spikes, helmet, shinguard, _____

   b) Write another word in each category.

WORDS IN HISTORY

Umpire comes from the Latin <u>non</u> <u>par</u> meaning 'not equal'. It means 'an impartial third party who decides a dispute between two others'. It came to be spelled **numpire**. The **n** was dropped when it became attached to the **a** in **an umpire**.

2. **a)** Write three compound words you associate with the sports pictured below.
   b) Choose another sport of your own and write three compounds that belong to it.

3. A **kneepad** is used in several sports to protect the athletes, for example, in soccer, volleyball, and hockey. Choose a sport and list **five** types of protective equipment team players might wear.

4. **Are they one word or two?** Check these words in your dictionary to see if they are spelled as one word.

    a) hotdog
    b) armload
    c) fishstick
    d) goaltender
    e) ratepayer

5. **a)** Every sport uses special words to describe players and playing situations. Name the sport for each of the words below.

southpaw	jump shot	end run
slapshot	penalty shot	love

    b) Explain the meaning of each word in one or two sentences.

6. **a)** Write a cheer for your favourite sport.

Example: *Lean to the left*
                 Lean to the right
                 Stand up, sit down
                 Fight, fight, fight!

    b) Design a banner or pennant you can wave when you cheer for your team.

Hint!
Compound words are formed by joining two base words.

49

11 Homophones

cereal serial

course
weighed
because*
fossil
cereal
wade
vary
missed
straight
principle
would
coarse
serial
wood
principal
strait
mist
very

Bone into Stone

Hello, everyone! This is Nigel DeBarlo for Kids' Report. Would you like to know what I'm standing in? It's a giant, fossil footprint, perhaps made by a dinosaur who liked to wade in the soft mud of a river bank in the morning mist.

We now know that dinosaurs liked to travel in family groups, because we have found many of their footprints close together. Using the principle that the depth of the footprint will vary according to the size of the dinosaur, scientists can estimate how much the animal weighed. To scientists, these footprints and the layers of rock above my head are much like a serial on tv. Each layer is a separate episode in Earth's history.

Of course, wood, bone, and other hard substances are the principal fossilized materials. When a dinosaur bone is found, it is wrapped in coarse cloth which has been soaked in plaster, then transported straight to a museum.

Very rarely, softer parts of plants and animals are preserved. For example, in the Arctic, entire woolly mammoths have been found frozen in ancient ice. By examining their stomach contents, we can even tell which fossil cereal they ate. Walking in the footprints of the dinosaurs is an experience not to be missed!

Observing Patterns

1. Write the list words that fit these definitions.
   a) breakfast food _____
   b) the person who is in charge of a school _____
   c) petrified remains of a prehistoric animal or plant _____
   d) narrow channel joining two larger bodies of water _____
   e) arranged in a series _____

*Because is one of the 25 most frequently misspelled words.

50

2. a) Write the pairs of list words that rhyme with the following.

should   _____   _____
horse   _____   _____
jade   _____   _____
bury   _____   _____
fist   _____   _____
freight   _____   _____

b) Add one more rhyming word to each set.

3. Write the three pairs of list words that are alike <u>except for one letter</u>.

4. Complete each sentence with list words that best fit the sentences.

a) This piece of rock is _____ special to me _____ it contains a bone _____ .

b) My aunt asked if I _____ like to go to the baseball game with her. Of _____ , I said I'd like to go. I wouldn't have _____ the game for anything.

Discovering Patterns

course weighed because fossil cereal wade vary missed straight principle would coarse serial wood principal strait mist very

1. Write the eight homophone pairs from the word list.

Use a dictionary to find the meaning of any of the homophones you are unsure of.

2. Write a homophone for each word below.

won   for   some   grate   blue

Homophones are words that sound the same but have different spellings and meanings.

POWERBOOSTER

* Homophones are words that sound the same but have different meanings and sometimes different spellings.

51

Exploring Patterns

1. Complete each sentence with the correct **homophones**.

a) The team (would, wood) be (vary, very) disappointed if you (mist, missed) the championship game.

b) We (wade, weighed) the three bowls of (serial, cereal) in order to study the (principal, principle) of mass.

c) The (course, coarse) texture of the (wood, would) made it necessary to use sandpaper.

d) The water temperature in the Hudson (Strait, Straight) will (very, vary), of (course, coarse), with the time of year.

e) I like to (weighed, wade) (strait, straight) into the water as the early morning (mist, missed) is rising from the lake.

f) The (principle, principal) asked us to record the (serial, cereal) numbers of our locks.

2. a) Read the dictionary entry below for the list word **straight**.

straight (strāt) **1** without a bend or curve. **2** in an erect position; upright. **3** in proper order or condition. **4** without delay. **5** in poker, a sequence of five cards.

b) Write the number of the definition from the entry which fits the use of **straight** in each sentence below.

Sit straight in your chairs please. _____
When he looked at his cards he could scarcely believe his eyes—a straight flush! _____
Draw a straight line between the two points on the diagram. _____
It is important to keep your bank records straight at all times. _____
Don't forget to come straight home after school. _____

3. What's wrong? These advertisements have got their homophones mixed up. Correct them by using the right homophones. Use your dictionary if you are unsure.

a) Bird cages on special—very cheep!

b) Fresh honey—our quality can't bee topped!

c) Assorted gum—you chews

d) Chocolate sundaes prepared while you weight

e) Midsummer sail—All beechwear reduced

52

4. Scientists who study dinosaur fossils are like detectives. They have fragile clues to help them piece together the story of how dinosaurs lived and died. Suppose you came upon dinosaur tracks with these characteristics:

a) one set is large and deep, one is smaller and shallow

b) one set of footprints is much closer together than the other

c) the two sets run parallel for a time, then the larger set crosses the smaller

d) there is only one set of tracks at the end—the larger one; now the footprints are closer together

What do you think happened? Write a report describing your idea of what the two sets of tracks mean.

Challenges with Words

1. The computer ran a spell check on the paragraph below, but didn't catch the **homophone** errors. Use the Super Words to correct the mistakes.

One of my assistance held the rock stationery while the other split it with a hammer. I rung my hands in anxiety. Would we find a perfectly formed fossil fern inside? Would each vane stand out? Would this be an important discovery or just a miner find? Our team was certainly overdo for some good luck!

2. *Due ewe no sum* of the homophones *four* these words? *Right the rite won.* Then, correctly rewrite the instructions for this question.

mussel _____   least _____
sight _____   profit _____
palette _____

3. Use the letters from the word stationary below to make words from the letters. You can use a letter more than once.

Score **1 point** for each letter used in a word.

Add **4 points** if you filled in all the blank spaces. Plurals can be used.

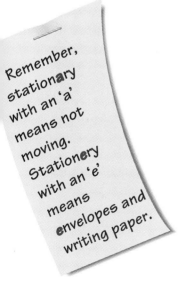

overdue
vein
stationary
assistants
wrung
minor

Remember, stationary with an 'a' means not moving. Stationery with an 'e' means envelopes and writing paper.

Points

a) s t _ _ _ _   _____
b) n _ _ _ _   _____
c) t _ _ _ _   _____
d) r a _ _ _ _ _   _____
e) y _ _ _ _   _____

SCORE CARD

25   *perfect score*
20   *good score*
15   *average*

Homophone Dictionary
a   –
b   –   be, bee
c   –   cot, caught
d   –   ?
e   –   ?

4. Make a homophone dictionary. Write a pair of homophones for as many letters of the alphabet as you can.

5. Write a story using some of the homophones below. See if a partner can supply the correct spelling.

past - passed
prince - prints
reign - rain - rein
some - sum
moat - mote
waste - waist
guest - guessed
hoard - horde

ultrasound
biosphere
re-entry

6. New words have to be found all the time to describe changes, discoveries, and inventions in science. Complete each sentence below with the correct new word.

   a) The _____ is the layer on the planet Earth that supports life.

   b) _____ waves are used to diagnose many medical conditions.

   c) _____ is the returning of a rocket or spacecraft into Earth's atmosphere after a flight in outer space.

12 Looking Back

STUDY STEPS

LOOK
SAY
COVER
WRITE
CHECK

Make a list of difficult words.

Here is a list of challenging words from Units 7–11.

important	fourth	certainly	surprise
heard	necessary	irrigate	poison
doubt	different	co-operate	attitude
champions	success	choice	because
very	yourself	blurred	satisfaction

1. Use the Study Steps for each word. Your teacher will then dictate the words.

2. Complete this report for a school newspaper with words from the Study List.

Soccer Champs

Have you _____ the great news? For the _____ year in a row, our girls' soccer teams are district _____ ! The victories come as no _____ to the coaches. They say the _____ of both teams is due to a positive _____ and a willingness to _____ both on and off the field. There is little _____ that most of the players, if given a _____ , would play soccer before any other sport.

The girls practise as long as _____ before a match _____ they know how _____ it is to be _____ well-prepared. They find great _____ in working on new plays and trying _____ types of shots.

Buy a ticket for the tournament and see for _____ what great teams are representing our school.

3. **a)** Write the review words that contain double consonants. Circle the double consonants in each word.

   b) Which review word contains a double vowel?

4. Complete each review word.

dou _ t   p _ _ son   bec _ _ se   ne _ e _ _ ary

f _ _ rth   diff _ r _ nt   s _ _ pri _ e   c _ rt _ _ nly

5. Write words with the /ôr/ sound that mean the opposite of the words below.

giant   ceiling   backward

6. Complete each analogy with a word containing the /ôr/ sound.
   a) **me** is to **myself** as **you** is to _____
   b) **cold** is to **hot** as **trivial** is to _____
   c) **second** is to **third** as **third** is to _____
   d) **Sir John A. MacDonald** is to **prime minister** as **Champlain** is to _____

7. Write each sentence using the correct homophone from the pair given.

   a) (wood, would)   How _____ you like to make the birdhouse with this _____ ?
   b) (wade, weighed)   It was difficult to _____ through the muddy swamp because our equipment _____ so much.
   c) (serial, cereal)   We copied the _____ number from the bottom of the box of _____ .
   d) (mist, missed)   We _____ seeing the family of ducks swim past because they were hidden by the _____ on the lake.

8. a) Copy the chart into your notebook. Sort the words below into the correct categories.

/ėr/ as in **first, alert, learn, burn**	/är/ as in **chart**	/oi/ as in **soil, employ**	/ou/ as in **sour, tower**

fertile	hardly	urgent	heard
drowned	dirty	moist	enjoyable
target	annoyed	foul	powerful
avoid	crouch	sparkling	department

   b) Add two more words which fit the patterns to each column.

Dictionary Skills

Check your dictionary for the symbols used for other sounds.

1. **Spelling Chart:** If you know how to pronounce a word but do not know how to spell it, the spelling chart in a dictionary will help you. The chart gives the common spellings of English sounds. Study the spelling chart below.

Sound	Common Spelling of English Sounds
/ā/	**age**, **ad**, str**aigh**t, r**eig**n, n**eigh**bour
/f/	**f**at, **ph**one, cof**f**ee, laug**h**ter, go**ph**er
/h/	**h**e, **wh**o, **wh**y, (hwi)
/m/	**m**e, cli**mb**ing, su**mm**er, sole**mn**
/n/	**gn**aw, **kn**ife, **n**ut, **pn**eumonia
/s/	**c**ent, **ps**alm, **sc**ience, **s**word
/ü/	**new**, r**u**le, f**oo**d, fr**ui**t
/yü/	**you**, curf**ew**, **eu**chre, **Yu**le

2. It may be necessary to try more than one spelling of a sound before locating the word you want in a dictionary. Which word from the spelling chart would help you to find each of the following words? The part of the word that would make it difficult to spell and locate is underlined.

  a) <u>kn</u>ew   **b)** <u>ph</u>oto
  c) <u>c</u>ertainly   **d)** st<u>oo</u>l
  e) bo<u>mb</u>   **f)** <u>sc</u>issors
  g) <u>wh</u>ole   **h)** w<u>eigh</u>ed
  i) f<u>eu</u>d   **j)** autu<u>mn</u>

3. **Pronunciation Key:** If you know how to spell a word but are unsure of how to say it, the pronunciation guide in brackets following each entry word will help you. When you understand the symbols, you will be able to pronounce a word even if you have never heard it before.

Study the pronunciation key on page 173 of your text. Use it to write the entry word that matches each set of pronunciation symbols.

$$(dwôrf) \quad (kw\bar{o}t) \quad (dout) \quad (skôr'bôrd')$$

$$(m\bar{i}'gr\bar{a}t) \text{ or } (m\bar{i} \, gr\bar{a}t')$$

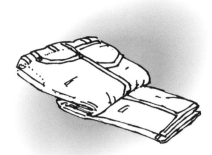

4. Homophone pairs are given identical pronunciation symbols in the dictionary. Write the homophone pairs that are represented by these symbols.

(hōl) (strāt) (wu̇d) (jēnz)

In My Opinion

1. a) Columnists in newspapers and magazines often write about their own opinions on issues. What opinions do you have about issues which interest you? For example, how do you feel about air pollution? Wearing bicycle helmets? Other issues? List three issues you feel strongly about.

b) Choose one issue and brainstorm for the words and phrases which describe and explain how you feel.

c) Now try writing a short article explaining your opinion. You might want to talk to other people (friends, teachers, and so on) and ask their opinions. If you can, use some of their ideas in your article.

2. Use a dictionary to check your spelling when you proofread your article.

Grammar Power

1. Subjects and Predicates: The subject is what the sentence is about. Ask yourself **who** or **what** did it and you will find the subject.

Here are some sentences that need subjects. Add your own.

    a) _____ roared out of the driveway.
    b) _____ danced around the room.
    c) _____ ate six bowls of popcorn.
    d) _____ chewed up my homework.

The **predicate** of a sentence is what the subject did, or had. Ask yourself **what** did the person or thing do and you will find the predicate.

2. Here are some sentences that need predicates. Add your own.

    a) The huge, black rhinocerous _____ .
    b) Our school bus _____ .
    c) My friend Jamal _____ .
    d) The team captain _____ .

3. Commas: Commas indicate a pause in a sentence. You can hear when a comma is necessary when you read your sentences out loud. Commas are often used for the following:

- to separate words in a list:
  I love pizza, pitas, and popcorn.

- to join two sentences with and, so, or but:
  I love ice cream, but hate sherbet.

- in dialogue:
  "Help," screamed Joe.

- after an introductory word:
  However, I'll eat it if there is nothing else.

Read these sentences with a partner. Decide where you should put commas.

    a) My dad bought oranges apples pears and broccoli at the store.
    b) "Bob" I shouted " where are you going?"
    c) Hopefully we will have a beautiful day for our field trip.
    d) The dog was hungry so he ate my hat.

Did you and your partner agree? Can you think of any rules for adding commas?

Proofing Power

1. Proofread the paragraph below, then rewrite it correcting all the spelling errors that you find.

In my opinion, it is vary importent to try to make yerself a sucess, whether it be your team being the league champiens or just being good in school. I do my best in everything and, if nessecary, I practise until I imporve.

You certinly have a choise in what you do. Try something new. Maybe you will suprise yourself. Everyone has diffrent talents. You just need to have a positive atitude and be ready to coperate. Why? Becuse it will give you the satasfaction of knowing that you can work as a team.

Well, I'm done. Did you enjoy my little lecture?

13 Plurals

letters glass**es** cit**ies**

alphabets
people
letters
pictures
libraries
cities
systems
codes
beaches
changes
branches
signs
glasses
thousands
addresses
shelves
themselves
centuries

Pictures into Alphabets

Hi! This is Amy Wong. I'm writing invitations to my friends for a party next week.

Did you ever stop to think that without alphabets, we couldn't write at all? All early writing systems began with pictures carved in stone or clay. Alphabets like our own, where the letters represent the sounds we make when we speak, developed later. But some modern road signs still use picture codes, where a symbol stands for food, or gas. And the Chinese writing system has thousands of symbols—each one representing a word.

Our alphabet began three thousand years ago, when Phoenician ships brought a system of letters from the Middle East to the ports and beaches of Greece. In Greek cities such as Athens and Sparta, writing flourished, and libraries were built with shelves of stories, plays, poetry, and history.

Our alphabet has undergone many changes over the centuries, as branches of it spread to many countries. Each group of people changed the alphabet to suit themselves. I'm just glad we have it to write important things like invitations.

Now, if I can just find my glasses I'll check those addresses on my invitations!

Observing Patterns

1. Complete each analogy with a list word.
   a) **numbers** are to **counting** as _____ are to **writing**
   b) **cars** are to **garages** as **books** are to _____
   c) **hearing aids** are to **ears** as _____ are to **eyes**
   d) **forests** are to **animals** as _____ are to **people**

2. Write the list words that have double consonants. Circle the double consonants.

3. Write the list words you would find in the dictionary between the words **bath/coffee**.

Discovering Patterns

alphabets people letters pictures libraries cities systems codes beaches changes branches signs glasses thousands addresses shelves themselves centuries

1. Examine the following plural list words. What has been added to the base words to form the plural?

alphabets   letters   pictures   systems

signs   thousands   changes   codes

2. Write the following list words. Beside each, write the singular form. How is the plural formed in words which end in **f**?

yourselves   shelves

3. Write the following list words. Beside each, write the singular form. How is the plural formed in words which end in the letters **ss** or **ch**?

addresses   glasses   branches   beaches

4. Write these list words and the singular form of each. How is the plural formed in words which end in a **consonant plus y**?

cities   libraries   centuries

5. The word **people** represents an irregular plural form. What is the singular of **people**?

The word **people** can also be made plural as in 'All the **peoples** of the world need to work for peace'.

POWERBOOSTER

- Most words form the plural by adding **s** to the singular form.
- When a word ends in **f**, form the plural by changing **f** to **v** and adding **-es** (**shelf** to **shelves**).
- Words which end in **ss** or **ch** form the plural by adding **-es** (**glasses**, **branches**).
- Words which end in **consonant + y** form the plural by changing **y** to **i** and adding **-es** (**cities**, **babies**).

Exploring Patterns

1. Change each word on the alphabet word pole to its plural form.

a	llergy	_____
l	eaf	_____
p	each	_____
h	alf	_____
a	ddress	_____
b	attery	_____
e	lf	_____
t	erritory	_____

2. Here are some words that have irregular plural forms. Use the plural form of each picture word below in a sentence.

a)

b)

c)

d)

e)

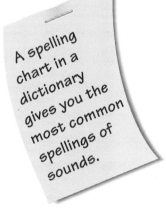

A spelling chart in a dictionary gives you the most common spellings of sounds.

3. Examine the partial spelling chart carefully. Write the word from the chart that would help you find each list word below in the dictionary. The difficult part of each list word is underlined.

al<u>ph</u>abets   s<u>y</u>stems   si<u>g</u>ns   <u>c</u>ities

Sound	Common Spelling
/f/	**f**at, cof**f**ee, go**ph**er, cou**gh**
/i/	**i**n, s**ie**ve, b**ui**ld, h**y**mn
/ī/	**ey**e, b**uy**ing, al**ig**n, l**ie**
/s/	**ps**alm, **c**ent, ma**ss**ive, ni**ce**

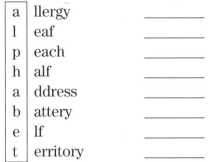

4. Complete this passage with list words. The beginning of each word has been given.

L_____ have existed for th_____ of years. Over the c_____ , information has been stored in the form of l_____ , p_____ , and books. Today's libraries show s_____ of many ch_____ from the past. Instead of locating information only on sh_____ , books are often recorded in c_____ on computer s_____ . P_____ who live in larger towns and c_____ will often find br_____ of the main library near their homes. Whether people are looking for the a_____ of large companies or amusing th_____ with books, records, and tapes, the library is a friendly, helpful place.

5. 'A' is for .... Work with a partner to make an alphabet booklet on a topic that interests you both.

Example: **The ABC of Sports**

'*A*' *is for Archery*
'*B*' *is for Basketball*
'*C*' *is for Cross-country skiing*

or a **Kid's Complaints** *alphabet book.*

'*A*' *is for All out of toothpaste*
'*B*' *is for Baby-sitting my little brother*
'*C*' *is for....*

Challenges with Words

1. a) Write the Super Words which complete the analogies below.
   clothes are to **drawers** as **books** are to _____
   facts are to **encyclopedia** as **definitions** are to _____
   long is to **odds** as **wild** is to _____
   landscape is to **paintings** as **English** is to _____
   money is to **banker** as **books** are to _____
   note is to **sung** as **word** is to _____

b) What do you notice about the order of the Super Words you have written?

pronounced
dictionaries
languages
librarian
guesses
bookshelves

2. Complete the missing plurals in the following sentences. The plural endings have been given.

a) There were three _ _ _ _ _ **sses** to the robbery.

b) The rich _ _ _ _ _ **sses** bought crystal _ _ _ **sses** in Paris.

c) Go and buy some _ _ _ _ **es** of bread at one of the _ _ _ _ _ _ **es** in town.

3. Make your own alphabet code. Draw a symbol for each letter of the alphabet. Then write a sentence, paragraph, or riddle in your code. Give it to a partner to decipher.

4. a) A librarian is a person who helps with research. Do you know these other -**ian** people?

Someone who doesn't eat meat is a _____ian.

A person who makes us laugh is called a _____ian.

If our dog is sick, we take it to a _____ian.

When you cross the street you are a _____ian.

b) Choose a word that ends in -**ian** and names an occupation. Write a job description for this person.

Example: 'A veterinarian is a person who cares for sick animals and ....'

5. All of the new words come from the world of computers. Write the words that fit the clues.

a) a computer chip that controls the operation of a computer

b) information stored in a computer

c) computer art that you can use in your own work

Remember to check a dictionary if you are unsure of how to spell a word.

14

Contractions and Possessives

you're student's players'

doesn't
you're
penalty
league
they've
players'
students'
referee's
football
soccer
goalie's
injury
shouldn't
student's
he'd
player's
hasn't
opponents'

Soccer to Football

Hi, everybody. This is Alexander Douglas. I bet <u>you're</u> all wondering why I'm standing in the middle of the <u>penalty</u> area of a <u>soccer</u> field. Well, it's not to catch the ball. That's the <u>goalie's</u> job. I'm here to tell you about soccer and <u>football</u>.

It all started in England, over three hundred years ago. In those days, <u>injury</u> was part of the game. There was no <u>referee's</u> whistle to stop the shin-kicking or tackling. There was only one rule: players <u>shouldn't</u> pick up the ball. In 1823, a <u>student's</u> wild impulse changed the game. William Ellis became so frustrated when he missed a kick that he picked up the ball and ran toward the <u>opponents'</u> goal. The <u>students'</u> wild cheering spurred Ellis on. <u>He'd</u> just invented football.

Over the years, while soccer became less violent, football stuck to the old rough and tumble rules. Eventually, a <u>player's</u> equipment made the game safer. Although football is played everywhere in North America, it <u>hasn't</u> caught on in the rest of the world, where people prefer soccer. In some countries, such as England, <u>they've</u> formed an amateur and a professional <u>players'</u> <u>league</u> in nearly every city.

It <u>doesn't</u> matter which game you play, kicking a ball around is fun. This is Alexander Douglas, kicking off for now!

Observing Patterns

1. Write the list words that mean the opposite of the words below.

teacher's   has   does   reward   teammates'

2. Write the list words that have three syllables.

3. Write the seven list words that fall between **photograph** and **suddenly** in the dictionary.

64

4. Write the list words that rhyme with the words below.

pure deed save fatigue

5. Complete each sentence with list words.

a) In both hockey and _____ , the _____ job is to stop the _____ shots from crossing the goal line.

b) Soccer, which is a form of _____ , is the world's most popular spectator sport.

c) You _____ argue over a call. The _____ decision is final.

Discovering Patterns

doesn't you're penalty league they've
players' students' referee's football
soccer goalie's injury shouldn't student's
he'd player's hasn't opponents'

1. A **contraction** is a shortened form of two words. Write the list words that are contractions. Beside each contraction, write the two words from which it is made. Notice which letter or letters have been replaced by an apostrophe. *For example: you're—you are.*

2. Write the list words that end in **apostrophe** and **s ('s)**. These words mean 'belonging to...' and are called **possessives**. Singular possessives are formed from words by adding **'s** to the base word. Underline the base word in each possessive. *For example: player's.*

3. Write the list words that end in **s** and **apostrophe (s')**. These words are all plural possessives. Underline the plural form of each word. What has been added to the plural form to make it possessive? *For example: students'.*

POWERBOOSTER

- A contraction is a shortened form of two words. One or more letters are taken out and replaced by an apostrophe, as in **you're**, **you are**.
- The possessive form, meaning 'belonging to', is made by adding **apostrophe** and **s ('s)** to the singular base word, as in **player's**.
- The plural possessive is formed by adding an **apostrophe (')** to the plural form of the base word, as in **players'**.

Exploring Patterns

1. Use the possessive form to complete each of the following statements.

    a) The equipment belonging to the player is the _____ equipment.

The equipment belonging to the players is the _____ equipment.

    b) The score kept by the student is the _____ score.

The scores kept by the students are the _____ scores.

    c) The picture of the hockey team is the _____ picture.

The pictures of the hockey teams are the _____ pictures.

2. Complete each analogy with a list word.

    a) **reward** is to **bonus** as **punishment** is to _____

    b) **province** is to **country** as **team** is to _____

    c) **home plate** is to **baseball** as **goal** is to _____ and _____

Remember an analogy is a comparison between things that are alike in some way.

3. Both plural and possessive nouns may end in **s**. Choose either the plural or possessive form of the word in brackets that best fits the sentence. Write the sentence.

    a) A _____ mitt is sturdy and well padded. (catchers, catcher's)

    b) We called in some respected _____ to decide the game. (experts, expert's)

    c) The _____ shape was most unusual. (helmet's, helmets)

    d) We lost several _____ in the river behind the field. (baseball's, baseballs)

4. Combine words from each soccer ball to form as many contractions as possible. From your list of contractions, choose four to use in sentences.

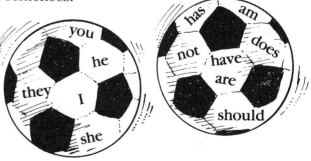

Example: *they + would = they'd*
         They said they'd be here by noon.

5. **a)** Imagine you were present when William Ellis raced down the field <u>carrying</u> a soccer ball in 1823. Write an interview with Ellis after the game. You might want to ask some questions, such as: "William, why did you pick up the ball?"

b) You may wish to role play the interview with a partner before you start writing. Often, good ideas are sparked by listening to what someone else says.

Challenges with Words

1. **a)** Use the Super Words to complete the letter below.

Dear Toshiko,

Have I told you about the _____ soccer team I play for called 'Truckers'? All the _____ names in our league have something to do with vehicles. Everybody plays hard, and _____ at our practices is almost 100%. Our coach _____ played professional soccer when he was younger. He really has a _____ attitude toward the game. We're winning four out of five games! But I _____ ramble on about soccer. How about you—what are you doing these days?

Yours truly,

Kim

b) Write a letter to one of your friends. What are you doing these days? You might want to address your letter and send it.

mustn't
professional
could've
amateur
attendance
squads'

═══ **WORDS IN HISTORY** ═══

How fond of sports are you? If you're an **amateur**, you're very fond of sports. **Amateur** comes from the Latin word <u>amator</u>, meaning 'lover'.

2. Look in your dictionary to see if you can find the origin of the word **professional**.

pass
goal
penalty
off

3. Sports go-betweens: Match a word from the box with each set of words below to form two sports expressions.

Example: *drive/goal   line drive   goal line*

a) kick/sides   **b)** shot/major
c) post/field   **d)** line/forward

4. The writer of this paragraph on soccer history didn't seem to know much about using apostrophes. **Proofread** and rewrite it with your corrections.

Ancient football was played with a cows bladder or perhaps an enemys' skull as the ball! The game was called 'Kicking the Danes 'Head' in 11th century Britain. Most early games' were just free-for-all's, with hundreds' of player's on each side. Football matche's between two town's teams would start with the ball placed halfway between. The game was won when the ball reached the centre of one towns' square.

5. Fill in the chart below. Then use the information you have organized to sum up the differences between soccer and football in a sentence or two. You may want to use reference books to help you.

Game	Soccer	Football
Equipment		
Field		
Players		
Scoring		
Penalties		

15

Consonant Sound

sh ti ci

ship action ancient

distance
invention
patient
dialling
speech
ownership
conversation
exhibition
telephone
action
nation
wouldn't
education
official
ancient
shall
social
shouted

Sound into Electricity

Hi! This is Beverley Windsor on the phone for Kids' Report.

Alexander Graham Bell invented the <u>telephone</u> in 1876, after years of <u>patient</u> work and experimentation. At the same time, many other inventors were trying to turn <u>speech</u> into electrical impulses that could be transmitted over a wire. Bell registered his patent first, so he claimed <u>ownership</u> of the <u>invention</u>.

Today, I'm here at the <u>official</u> opening of the telephone <u>exhibition</u> at the Science Museum. The display shows how, in <u>ancient</u> times, people <u>shouted</u> when they wanted to talk to someone at a <u>distance</u>. Now, just by the simple <u>action</u> of <u>dialling</u> a number, I can have a <u>conversation</u> with someone on the other side of the <u>nation</u>. I can even talk to someone in an airplane high above my head.

In Canada, telephone communication is important for business, <u>education</u>, and our <u>social</u> life. Most people <u>wouldn't</u> be able to manage without at least one telephone in their homes. Perhaps, in the future, we <u>shall</u> never go anywhere without our phones.

This is Beverley Windsor hanging up for Kids' Report.

Observing Patterns

1. Write the list words that have these base words.

   exhibit   converse   invent
   act   educate   own

2. Write the list words that mean the opposite of the words below.

   whispered   impatient   modern   unofficial

Working out analogies helps develop thinking skills.

3. Complete each analogy with a list word.
   a) **kilogram** is to **mass** as **kilometre** is to _____
   b) **eye** is to **sight** as **tongue** is to _____
   c) **city** is to **province** as **province** is to _____
   d) **computer** is to **keyboarding** as **telephone** is to _____

4. Fill in the missing letters to write the list words below.

   sp ___ h   tel ___ one   so __ al   s ___ ted

Discovering Patterns

distance invention patient dialling
speech ownership conversation
exhibition telephone action nation
wouldn't education official
ancient shall social shouted

1. a) Many of the list words contain the sound /sh/. This sound
   can be spelled in a number of ways. Make a chart in your
   notebook like the one below. Sort list words with the sound
   /sh/ into the correct categories.

/sh/ spelled **sh**	/sh/ spelled **ti**	/sh/ spelled **ci**

   b) Add two other words that fit the patterns to each column.

POWERBOOSTER

- The sound /sh/ can be spelled **sh** as in **show** and **wish**, **ti** as in **nation**,
  and **ci** as in **special**.

Exploring Patterns

1. Verbs can often be changed to nouns by adding **-ion** or **-ation**. When one of these forms is added to a verb ending in **e**, the final **e** is dropped, as in **combine—combination**.

a) Complete the chart below by changing the verbs to nouns.

Verb	Noun
invent	_____
create	_____
educate	_____
investigate	_____
converse	_____

b) Use four of the nouns above in sentences.

2. a) Construct a word web for the list words **telephone** and **conversation**.

3. Complete this paragraph with list words. Some of the beginning letters have been included for you. Use each list word only once.

The modern t_____ makes Alexander Graham Bell's i_____ seem a_____ . Businesses can now hold long _____ meetings with people from various parts of the _____ . The _____ is heard by each person through a conference line. Not only o_____ business but also s_____ calls are helped by modern telephones. If you are not a p_____ type of person, and hate _____ the numbers of all your friends, you could program your phone to do the job for you. You could also record your s_____ and leave it on an answering machine. That way, you _____ miss important calls. With so many benefits provided by the modern telephone, _____ of at least one phone is almost a necessity.

4. Unscramble the syllables on each telephone to find list words.

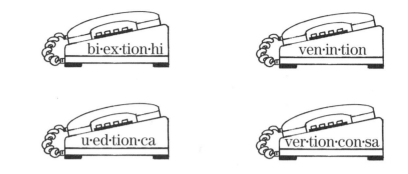

5. Phone Poems: Many words rhyme with phone, such as **loan**, **own**, and **alone**. Write as many rhyming words as you can. Then try to write a rhyming verse about phones.

Example:

Whenever I get on the phone,
I hear my parents start to groan...

OR

I need a phone
Of my own...

commercial
beneficial
impatient
efficient
artificial
communication

Challenges with Words

1. Use the Super Words that are similar in meaning to replace the underlined words in the paragraph below.

In a recent <u>message</u> from a friend, I learned that your property could be used for <u>business</u> purposes. You could make <u>good</u> use of your time by planning to sell <u>imitation</u> plants and flowers on the premises. Don't feel <u>restless</u> about the amount of time this would require to plan. It will eventually be a very <u>favourable</u> investment for you.

2. Do you turn into a fire-breathing dragon when you have to wait for someone to answer the telephone? List ten words that describe **how you feel** when you are **impatient**.

Now rank your words in order from **least** to **most** impatient.

WORDS IN HISTORY

The prefix **bene-** means 'favourable' or 'helpful'. It comes from the Latin adverb <u>bene</u> meaning 'well'.

3. How well do you know these **bene-** words? Match the words in the box to the definitions.

a) a person who helps others

b) someone who inherits money

c) it's good for you

> beneficiary
> benefactor
> beneficial

4. The prefix **mal-** means the opposite of **bene-**.

Look up three **mal-** words in the dictionary and use them in sentences.

5. Imagine you have invented a remarkable new type of telephone. This is going to make history! Using all of the Super Words, write a glowing description of your new telephone. Make it sound like an advertisement you could use in a magazine, newspaper, or television commercial.

6. The new words all have something to do with telephone technology. Use each one to complete the sentences below.

a) When you hear a 'beep' on the line it means there is a

_____ _____ .

b) If you get a busy signal you can push _____ to call again.

c) A telephone number that anyone can call for free is a

_____ _____ number.

NEW WORDS

redial

call waiting

toll free

16

Suffixes

**-less -ness -ment
-ful -ly**

harm**less** ugli**ness** argu**ment**
care**ful** love**ly**

careful

gently

beautiful

forceful

broadcast

media

friendly

lovely

advertisement

harmless

hopeless

softness

amusement

ugliness

endless

awareness

argument

luckily

Television

This is Nigel DeBarlo, your <u>friendly</u> reporter, with an insider's view of the TV world.

Of all the modern <u>media</u>, television is considered to be the most <u>forceful</u> and controversial. Some see it as a <u>harmless</u> <u>amusement</u>, others as a <u>hopeless</u> wasteland of <u>ugliness</u>. I'm not going to take sides in that <u>argument</u>. <u>Luckily</u>, I work on a show which is <u>careful</u> to show things that are <u>beautiful</u>, and wants to <u>gently</u> raise kids' <u>awareness</u> of what's going on in the

world. I think that's more important than an <u>endless</u> <u>advertisement</u> about the <u>softness</u> of someone's <u>lovely</u> hands. Here at Kids' Report, we try to offer something special in each <u>broadcast</u>.

Nigel DeBarlo, signing off for Kids' Report.

Observing Patterns

1. Write the three-syllable list words. Place an accent (´) on the stressed syllable in each word.

2. Write the three list words that mean the opposite of their base words.

3. Write the list words that would be found in the dictionary between **absolutely** and **certainly**.

4. Write the list words that match these shapes.

74

Discovering Patterns

careful gently beautiful forceful broadcast media friendly lovely advertisement harmless hopeless softness amusement ugliness endless awareness argument luckily

1. **a)** Write these list words.

   harmless   softness   friendly

   b) Underline the base word in each. What is similar about the endings of these base words? What happens, if anything, to these base words when suffixes beginning with a consonant are added?

2. **a)** Write these list words.

   hopeless   amusement   lovely

   b) Underline the base word in each. What is similar about the endings in these base words? What happens, if anything, to these base words when suffixes beginning with a consonant are added?

3. **a)** Write the list word **argument**.
   b) Beside it, write its base word. What happens to the base word of **argument** when a suffix is added?

Do you need to add something to your conclusions in question two?

4. **a)** Write these list words.

   ugliness   beautiful

   b) Beside each word write its base word. What is similar about the endings of these base words? What happens to the base words when suffixes are added?

Hint! Drop the **e** in argue when adding ment.

POWERBOOSTER

* When a base word ends in a **consonant**, as in **soft**, or **consonant + e**, as in **hope**, no changes are made to the base word when adding a suffix that begins with a consonant.
* When a base word ends in a **consonant + y**, as in **ugly**, change the **y** to **i** when adding suffixes.
* In rare cases, such as in **argue**, when the base word ends in a **vowel + e**, drop the **e** when adding suffixes.

FIGHTING A BATTLE AGAINST YOUR PET'S FLEAS?

Exploring Patterns

1. Complete these advertisements with list words. Some of the beginning letters have been included.

    a) Put an end to <u>u</u>_____ ! Our secret formula furniture polish _____ shines your furniture and leaves it looking

_____ .

    b) Looking for some <u>a</u>_____ ? Our _____ staff will show you an _____ variety of games, puzzles, and books.

    c) Fighting a <u>h</u>_____ battle against your pet's fleas? Through _____ research we have developed a _____ collar for your pet. This collar is deadly to fleas but _____ to your cat or dog.

2. The suffix **-ness** changes an adjective into a noun. For example, when **-ness** is added to the adjective **ugly**, it becomes the noun **ugliness**.

Read each pair of sentences below. The underlined word is used as an adjective in the first sentence. Complete the second sentence by adding **-ness** to this adjective.

    a) Our new German shepherd seems very <u>happy</u>. He shows his _____ by wagging his tail and barking.

    b) You shouldn't be so <u>careless</u>. Your _____ could cause an accident.

    c) Are you <u>aware</u> of the programs offered by the town's recreation department? This booklet should help to increase your _____ .

    d) My friend Sarah is a pleasant person but she's very <u>lazy</u>. Her _____ cost her a good summer job.

3. Look up the meaning of **media** in the dictionary. Use this information to help you design a word web for **media**.

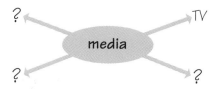

Remember, in words that end in y change the y to an I before adding -ness.

lovely— loveliness

76

faintly
patiently
sharply
absently

4. 'Tom Swifties' are jokes that use adverbs to create puns.

Example: "The sun is shining!" she said brightly.

Match the adverbs in the box to the sentences below to create 'Tom Swifties'.

  a) "Is the doctor here yet?" he asked _____ .
  b) "I must have passed out," she whispered _____ .
  c) "I missed the school bus," he said _____ .
  d) "These scissors have a good cutting edge," he announced _____ .

5. Debate: Is television good or bad? Write a short report that explains your own opinion.

I think television is good because ....

6. Survey: Take an opinion poll of your classmates.

Question: Do you think watching more than four hours of television each day is harmful to small children?

Name	Yes	No	Why
Kate			
Brian			

fuzziness
colourfully
transmission
assignment
motionless
videotape

Challenges with Words

1. a) Use Super Words as **antonyms** to correct the underlined words in the paragraph below.

The <u>reception</u> from the TV station last night was terrible! The <u>dully</u> dressed actors looked like gaudy clowns. The <u>clarity</u> of the picture made everyone look as if they were moving through dense fog. On top of that, the picture would suddenly be <u>moving</u> and then jerk into action again. We finally turned off the TV in disgust.

b) Write a <u>synonym</u> or an <u>antonym</u> for each of the two Super Words that were not used in the paragraph. Use these in a sentence or two of your own.

2. a) Descriptive Words: Many adjectives describe the feel, sound, or look of an object. Write words that describe the items below. Use the headings given.

Use words that are vivid and colourful. Use a thesaurus to help.

	Sight	Sound	Smell	Touch	Taste
a broken garbage bag					
a snowflake					
a new car					

b) Choose one of the objects and write a description of it using the words that you listed. Use a thesaurus to help. You may choose to write a descriptive paragraph or poem.

3. How many words can you **transmit**? Make new words by using the letters of the Super Word **transmission.**

You may change the order of the letters, but plurals are not allowed. We found twenty-six words. Can you find more?

4. Videotape is used to record sound and video images. Make a list of other devices, both old and new, which can be used to record information. Use the chart below to classify your list.

Old	New
	videotape
typewriter	
record	
	camcorder
?	?

5. Make two lists: good things about television; bad things about television. Now write a report on how you feel about television.

17

Base Words and Endings

copied studying

arranged

pitied

studying

published

copied

divided

crime

satisfying

illustrated

comic

characters

created

chuckled

produced

denied

bored

worried

strip

Roman Tablets into Comic Books

WHAP! POW! ZAP! This is Amy Wong with a feature on the fabulous <u>comic</u> <u>strip</u>. I became very interested in comics while I was <u>studying</u> them. Did you know that the Romans <u>produced</u> cartoons over 2000 years ago? ... Or that in the 16th century, <u>crime</u> comics were popular in Germany?

Comics are really <u>illustrated</u> stories. The story is <u>arranged</u> in panels, with each panel <u>divided</u> into several frames. Comics are usually <u>created</u> by writers and artists. The first comic book was <u>published</u> in 1933.

At first, comic books <u>copied</u> the popular newspaper strips, but by the 1940s, <u>characters</u> such as Wonder Women and other super-

heroes had appeared. During the 1950s, comics became so violent that many people <u>worried</u> that they were harmful, and <u>denied</u> comic books to their children. The comic book industry developed a code of self-censorship that still exists. Some comics are very <u>satisfying</u> reading, others are just fun to read when you're <u>bored</u>. I think anyone who has never <u>chuckled</u> over Calvin and Hobbes or Charlie Brown is to be <u>pitied</u>! BAM! This is Amy Wong signing off for Kids' Report.

Observing Patterns

1. Several list words contain the consonant sound /k/. Write the words which fit the following categories.

    a) /k/ at the beginning of the word, spelled **c**

    b) /k/ at the beginning of the word spelled **ch**

    c) /k/ at the middle of the word, spelled **ck**

2. Write the list words that contain double consonants. Circle the double consonants.

3. Complete each sentence with a list word which means the **opposite** of the underlined word.

　　a) My little brother was <u>fascinated</u> with the dinosaur exhibit but _____ with the pottery display.

　　b) "First, I <u>multiplied</u> the numbers by ten, then I _____ them by seven."

　　c) The fire <u>destroyed</u> the sculpture she had _____ .

Discovering Patterns

arranged pitied studying published copied divided crime satisfying illustrated comic characters created chuckled produced denied bored worried strip

1. Write the words below.

　　　　published, publishing　　tracked, tracking

Write the base word for each set. What is similar about the final two letters of these base words? What happens, if anything, when **-ed** or **-ing** is added to them?

2. Write these words.

　　　　arranged, arranging　　divided, dividing

Write the base word for each set. What is similar about their final two letters? What happens when **-ed** or **-ing** is added to them?

3. Write the following words.

　　　　worried, worrying　　satisfied, satisfying

Write the base word for each set. What is similar about their final two letters? What happens when **-ed** is added? What happens, if anything, when **-ing** is added?

POWERBOOSTER

- When a word ends in more than one consonant, as in **publish**, no changes are made in the base word when adding **-ed** or **-ing**.
- When a word ends in a **consonant + e**, as in **arrange**, drop the **e** before adding **-ed** or **-ing**.
- When a word ends in a **consonant + y**, as in **worry**, no changes are made when adding **-ing**. When adding **-ed**, change the **y** to **i**.

Exploring Patterns

1. **a)** Complete the chart below.

   b) Now write four more base words which end with **y** and add the endings.

Base Word	Add -ing	Add -ed
_____	studying	_____
_____	_____	chuckled
marry	_____	_____
_____	satisfying	denied
_____	_____	created
cry	_____	_____

2. Complete the following analogies with list words.
   a) practising is to **game** as _____ is to **examination**
   b) added is to **subtracted** as **multiplied** is to _____
   c) frowned is to **whined** as **smiled** is to _____
   d) accepted is to **refused** as **relieved** is to _____

3. **Mix and Match:** Make sentences by choosing a word from columns 1 to 4 and adding your own ideas for column 5. Using any combination of words you wish, create at least five sentences.

1	2	3	4	5
The	criminals	arranged	all of the	?
Your	cousins	created	because	?
My	uncle	divided	a famous	?
Her	friends	entertained	whenever	?
Some	comedians	published	a clever	?

Example: *Her cousins divided all of the candy into equal portions.*

4. **Shape Words:** Write the following list words in a way that reveals something about their meaning.

   copied   comic   worried   crime

SUPER WORDS

dialogue
photocopied
syndicated
horrified
satisfied
illustrator

5. Create a Comic Strip: Many people start drawing comics when they are very young. It's fun to illustrate a story you've written in comic strip format. First you need an interesting **character** or **characters**. Then you need a situation, a riddle, or a joke. Create your own comic strip. You might want to work with a partner or group, with each person specializing in one part of the work (art, script, handwriting).

Challenges with Words

1. **a)** Substitute the correct Super Word for each underlined word in the comic strip outline below.

The Case of the Disappearing Dentist

Frame 1: Dr. Pullem's assistant, Gunnar Bates, is <u>shocked</u> by the doctor's disappearance. He goes back to her office late at night.

Frame 2: He is not <u>happy</u> with the note the doctor left.

Frame 3: While searching for clues, he finds a file folder of <u>reproduced</u> articles. They are copies of the doctor's <u>distributed</u> dental advice column, 'The Root of It All'.

Frame 4: On some words in each column, a large tooth has been crudely drawn by an unknown <u>artist</u>. What could it mean?

Frame 5: Suddenly a noise stops him. He can hear two voices in angry <u>conversation</u> in the next room.

b) What will happen? Work with a partner to illustrate and produce the comic strip.

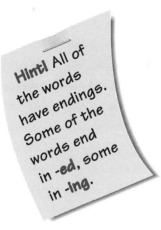
2. a) 'Y' not try these? Unscramble the letters in each section of the star, using the **i** from the centre, in each word.

b) Write the base word for each of the words you found. To find the name of these words, rearrange the **first** letters of these words.

Answer: _ _ _ _ _

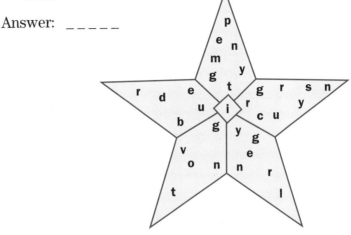

━━━━WORDS IN HISTORY━━━━

The Super Word **syndicated** once had a very different meaning: 'to judge or censure'. It comes from the Latin word <u>syndicare</u>, 'to censure'.

3. Write two modern meanings for the word **syndicate**. Use a dictionary to help you.

4. a) Write the word **comics** in the centre of a page. Then add words that relate to comics around it. Cluster the words in groups.

Example:

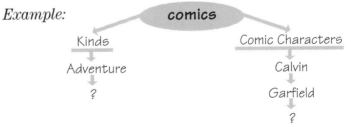

b) Use your words to write a short report about comics. Don't forget to proofread your report carefully.

5. All of the new words are two-word compounds. Write the words that fit the definitions below.

a) The ability of computers to think like humans is _____ .

b) A brief recorded remark that is replayed on radio or TV and has great impact on the public is a _____ _____ .

c) Three-dimensional projection controlled by computers is

_____ _____ .

STUDY STEPS

LOOK
SAY
COVER
WRITE
CHECK

Make your own list of challenging words.

Here is a list of challenging words from Units 13–17.

addresses	ancient	characters	illustrated
friendly	exhibition	worried	patient
official	argument	advertisement	beautiful
people	centuries	alphabets	league
pictures	doesn't	signs	referee's

1. Follow the Study Steps for each word. Your teacher will then dictate the words.

2. Complete the story with words from the Study List. Use each word only once. Some of the beginning letters have been included for you.

Last week I saw an _____ for the Museum where there was an _____ of a_____ Greek and Roman pottery. My friend Michael, who is not very p_____ , said he didn't want to go, but after a f_____ a_____ , he joined me. We followed the _____ to the exhibit, and were surprised to see so many _____ there. I was _____ we'd be bored waiting, but the _____ guide book, which was _____ with lovely _____ of the pottery, made the wait pleasant. The pottery exhibit was outstanding. The _____ on the pottery seemed almost lifelike. It _____ seem possible that pottery designed _____ ago could still be so _____ today.

3. Complete each sentence by adding one of the suffixes in the box to the base word in brackets. What changes do you make to the base words which end in **y**?

-less   -ness   -ment   -ful   -ly

a) She almost missed the bus, but (**lucky**) it was late.
b) I had an (**argue**) with my brother about cutting the grass.
c) Try to be (**care**) when you move those boxes.
d) The man's (**weary**) was shown by his slow, shuffling walk.

4. Complete these review words.

a) b _ _ _ t _ ful   **b)** a _ _ re _ _ es

c) an _ _ _ nt   **d)** pi _ t _ res

e) re _ e _ ee's   **f)** p _ _ p _ _

g) l _ _ g _ _   **h)** wo _ _ ied

5. Change the underlined words in each sentence from the **singular** to the **plural** forms. Remember that nouns and verbs may need to be changed.

a) A person who lives in a city might ride a streetcar to work.

b) My sister bought herself a new dress.

c) I found the address of the church and delivered the bunch of flowers.

6. Complete the word pole with words containing the /sh/ sound spelled **ci** or **ti**.

a) a person who is under a doctor's care   _ _ _ | i | _ _ _

b) very old   _ _ _ | i | _ _ _

c) another word for 'country'   _ _ _ | i | _ _

d) formal, as in 'This is an _____ entry form.'   _ _ _ _ | i | _ _

e) a product made for the first time   _ _ _ _ _ | i | _ _

f) what you receive through study, training, and experience   _ _ _ _ _ | i | _ _

7. **a)** Write the base words for these contractions.

can't   shouldn't   she'll   we're

b) Write the contractions for these base words.

does not   would not   you are   they have

8. Add the endings **-ed** and **-ing** to the verb on each disk.

divide   worry   publish   satisfy   handle

9. Rewrite each sentence by using the **possessive** form of the underlined phrase.

a) The mask worn by the goalie saved him from an injury.

b) We found leftover lunches and scrap paper in the lockers of the students.

c) She knocked over the goal post of her opponents by accident.

10. Make a word search puzzle for a partner with review words from your personal word lists and this unit.

Dictionary Skills

1. Inflected Forms: Words ending in **-s, -es, -er, -est, -ed**, and **-ing** are called **inflected forms**. Inflected forms do not appear in the dictionary as separate entries. To find inflected forms, look up the base word in the dictionary to which the ending was added. The inflected forms will be in dark, heavy type at the end of the entry. If no inflected forms appear, this is because the spelling of the entry word is not changed when the ending is added (walk, walked, walking).

Read the dictionary entry for the word **copy**.

> **cop•y** [kop′ ē] **1** anything made to be just like another. **2** make a copy. **3** follow as a pattern or model; imitate. *n. pl.* **cop•ies**; *v.* **cop•ied, cop•y•ing.**

a) What inflected forms of **copy** are given? Where do they appear in the entry?

b) Write the word you would locate in the dictionary to find each of these inflected forms.

cities   shelves   worried   satisfying

2. Suffixes and Prefixes: Words formed by adding a prefix or suffix are usually listed as separate entries in a dictionary.

When they are not, it is necessary to look up the meaning of the prefix or suffix and combine it with the meaning of the base word. Prefixes and suffixes are listed in alphabetical order with other dictionary entries.

Study the entries below for the prefix **un-** and the suffix **-ful**.

Example: prefix: **un-**, *meaning 'not, or the opposite of', as in* **unfair**.

suffix: **-ful**, *meaning 'full of', as in* **cheerful**.

a) Using the information in the entries, write a definition for **unfriendly** and **beautiful**.

b) What meanings are given in the dictionary for the suffixes **-less, -ly, -ness**?

Just the News

1. Sports and weather information are an important part of a radio news program. List all the facts and information you can think of for one of the following.

    a) today's weather

    b) a recent sports game at school or in your community.

2. Picture yourself as a radio news announcer. Write a news report for the topic you chose above. Be sure to use the **FIVE W**s (who? what? where? when? why?).

3. You might consider tape recording your report then playing it back to a partner.

Grammar Power

1. Avoiding Racial Bias: When we write we must not offend any ethnic groups. Use names that the groups themselves prefer. For example, use Native People, not Indians.

Don't name people as being part of a special group if it's not important in your writing.

Example: *The singer filled the hall with beautiful sound.*
not
The Italian singer filled the hall with beautiful sound.

The man purchased a new car.
not
The Korean man purchased a new car.

Look through your local newspaper for examples of the following:

a) racist language
b) non-racist language

2. Quotation Marks: When do we use quotation marks? We often use them for dialogue and put them around the words someone says.

Example: *"Listen to me," whispered Tama.*
He said it was "the most beautiful, but the hardest" goal he ever scored.

Use quotation marks to punctuate this dialogue.

a) It's time to get up my mother called.
b) Fifteen more minutes I grumbled, pulling the blankets over my ears.
c) It's already eight o'clock she insisted.
d) But I'm so tired I groaned. Leave me alone.
e) You're going to be late for school Mom warned.

3. Punctuation and quotation marks: We usually put commas, periods, question marks, and exclamation marks inside quotation marks.

Example: *"Help?" he shouted.*
               "Where are you?" I cried.
               "Over here," he answered, "in the cave."

Punctuate the sentences below.

a) "Is this your dog" the woman asked.

b) "Yes" I said. "This is Buster"

c) "Well please get Buster off my tulips" she said angrily. "He's breaking the stems"

d) "Buster" I screamed. "Come here"

Proofing Power

Read Jessica McGilvray's news report. Rewrite it correcting all of the spelling mistakes you can find. When you're finished, trade it with a partner and see if you both found the same errors in her report.

Hello, this is Jessica McGilvray reporting live from the City Museum on Main Street. A lot of poeple are here today to see the anshent alphebets exibition.

A museum offisial is very woried that some visitors are being careless with the exhibit. The patrons are having an arguement with the official right now. These charecters are really going at it! The museum employee is being very pateint and trying to explain that these beautifull artifacts are senturies old. The people keep ignoring the ilustrated sines that read, "Please do not touch!"

More on this story at eleven. This is Jessica McGilvray, signing off.

19

Verb Endings
Doubling Final Consonants

hidden winning

visible

film

shutter

slammed

dragged

preferred

image

fitted

hidden

camera

process

sensitive

tripped

beginning

winning

grabbed

permitting

forgetting

Light into Images

This is Alexander Douglas at the Photographers' Fair, with a report on the history of photography.

In the beginning, photography was a process used by painters to project a visible image on canvas. It wasn't until 1822, however, that the first permanent photo was made. Light-sensitive photographic paper, permitting a print from a negative, was invented later.

In those early days, whole families were dragged in front of the camera for portraits. They had to sit perfectly still until the photographer tripped the shutter, and it slammed shut. Hidden behind them were special clamps to hold their heads still.

Action photography was difficult. News photographers on their way to the scene, not only grabbed cameras, but also developing equipment. Forgetting this would be a disaster, as pictures had to be developed on the spot.

Over the next fifty years, there were many improvements in photography. Both 35mm film and colour film was invented and was soon preferred by many photographers. Now, cameras fitted with special lenses and automatic shutters make it easier to take prize-winning photographs.

Observing Patterns

1. Complete each sentence with a list word.

The children said they _____ peanut butter to sardines. Then they _____ over the toys, grabbed their jackets, _____ the door, and dashed out to play.

2. Write the list words that have three syllables. Place an accent (´) on the syllable that is stressed in each word.

3. Complete each comparison with a list word.
   a) **car** is to **gasoline** as **camera** is to _____
   b) **failure** is to **success** as **losing** is to _____
   c) **appear** is to **vanish** as **seen** is to _____
   d) **touched** is to **patted** as **grasped** is to _____
   e) **eye** is to **eyelid** as **camera** is to _____

Discovering Patterns

visible film shutter slammed dragged preferred image fitted hidden camera process sensitive tripped beginning winning grabbed permitting forgetting

1. Write the base word for each of the words below.

   slammed   dragged   tripped   winning

   What is similar about the last two letters of these single-syllable base words? What happens to the base word when **-ed** or **-ing** is added?

2. Write the base words for the words below.

   preferred   permitting   beginning   forgetting

   What is similar about the last two letters of these two-syllable base words? Where is the stressed syllable in these words? What happens to the base word when **-ed** or **-ing** is added?

3. Write the base words for these words.

   happening   limited   pardoned

   How are these base words similar to those of **preferred** and **beginning**? How are they different? What happens, if anything, to the base word when **-ed** or **-ing** is added?

POWERBOOSTER

- When a one-syllable word ends in a vowel and consonant, the consonant is doubled when **-ed** or **-ing** is added.
- When a two-syllable word ends in a vowel and consonant, and the final syllable is stressed, the final consonant is doubled when **-ed** or **-ing** is added.
- If the first syllable is stressed, the final consonant is not doubled.

Exploring Patterns

1. Complete the chart by adding **-ed** and **-ing** to the base words.

Base Word	Add -ed	Add -ing
drag	_____	_____
prefer	_____	_____
wonder	_____	_____
hop	_____	_____
skip	_____	_____
pardon	_____	_____
occur	_____	_____
anchor	_____	_____

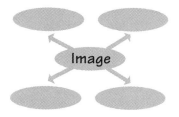

Remember that words which have **-ed** or **-ing** added are inflected forms.

2. Explain where you would look in the dictionary to check the spelling of each of the words below.

winning   admitted   forgetting

3. Many words can be enlarged by adding prefixes, suffixes, and other endings.

Example: visible   invisible   visibility

Enlarge the list word **image** in as many ways as possible. Use your dictionary as an aid.

4. Rewrite each sentence below, replacing the underlined words or phrases with list words that have similar meanings.

a) I am not <u>allowing</u> anyone to use the <u>photographic</u> equipment.

b) The actor <u>stumbled</u> over the rock, and <u>crashed</u> into the fence.

c) Right from the <u>start</u>, my baby sister <u>favoured</u> lots of noise and attention.

90

5. When you are remembering how to spell a word, your brain often acts like a camera. If the picture you have of a word is blurred or out of focus, you may write parts of the word incorrectly. Put these words back into focus by writing them correctly.

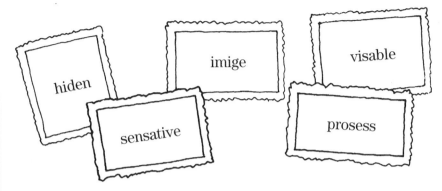

hiden

imige

visable

sensative

prosess

6. Look through newspapers, books, and magazines for photographs that capture a special moment in sports, reveal human feelings, or show a humorous incident. Write an explanation of why you would enter this photograph in a 'Best Picture of the Year' contest. Use some of the list words in this unit.

Challenges with Words

1. Match the correct Super Word to the clues below.
   a) this part of the camera is where light enters
   b) this varies the amount of light a) lets in
   c) this is given to photographic film to create an image
   d) this type of film is used to make a print
   e) this was what happened to exposed film
   f) this word should lighten things up

			p				g				
a			t								
	x	o									
		g				v					
		v				p					
i		l				n					

2. Diaphragm is a difficult word to spell because it has one silent letter and two letters which sound like /f/. Name all three letters.

Super Words

negative
diaphragm
aperture
developed
illuminating
exposure

━━━ WORDS IN HISTORY ━━━

The Super Word **negative** comes from the Latin <u>negare</u>, which means 'to say NO'.

3. Use your dictionary to help you write the meaning for the word **negative**, each time it is used below.
   a) The battery must be put in **negative** side down.
   b) "**Negative**," the police photographer replied to the judge.
   c) The X-ray showed only **negative** results.
   d) Oil from fingerprints can ruin a **negative**.
   e) The camera club got a **negative** response to the raffle idea.

4. a) Aperture means '**an opening**'. Make a word web for the word **aperture**.

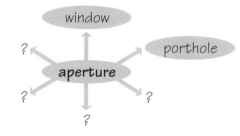

   b) Choose one of the words in your word web and list five more words which describe it.
   c) Write a short descriptive paragraph for part b), using as many of the words you have listed as you can.

5. Rewrite the paragraph below, changing all the present tense of the underlined verbs to the past tense.

> The shutter <u>snaps</u> just as the jaws of the giant crocodile also <u>crunches</u> its teeth. Suddenly, my feet <u>slip</u> out from under me. The crocodile <u>tries</u> to bite my leg but <u>catches</u> hold of my pants instead. Luckily, they <u>rip</u>. When I finally <u>arrive</u> back in civilization and <u>develop</u> my film, I <u>am</u> very disappointed. All I <u>end</u> up with <u>is</u> a close-up of the crocodile's nose! But I <u>am</u> not discouraged. I <u>decide</u> to return to Australia and…

6. Complete the story above in the past tense.

7. The new words are related to media and photography. Match the new words to the clues below.
   a) a three-dimensional photograph
   b) giving information by several different means at once, such as computer graphics, video, and CD-ROM
   c) recording sound and images on videotape

multimedia

videography

hologram

20 Schwa Vowels

item method

item
method
Canadian
admit
spirit
presently
manufacture
disgrace
banquet
sugarless
collected
delicious
panic
recent
syrup
American
dentist
Mexican

Sap into Chewing Gum

This is Beverley Windsor, with a report on chewing gum. I <u>admit</u> it! I love to chew gum! I used to be in <u>disgrace</u> with my <u>dentist</u>, because most gum is about 80 percent sugar. That's not very good for your teeth.

The <u>manufacture</u> of chewing gum has a long history. It comes from a <u>Mexican</u> tree, the Sapodilla, which was found in the <u>American</u> west. Today, sapodilla sap is <u>collected</u> by much the same <u>method</u> as <u>Canadian</u> maple <u>syrup</u>. Then it's boiled down into a gooey substance called chicle, mixed with <u>delicious</u> flavourings, and formed into strips, rectangles, or gum balls.

Gum manufacturers have many ways of making gum more appealing. Some gum packages contain a collector's <u>item</u>, such as a baseball card. Gum that squirts flavouring into your mouth, and gum that doesn't stick to your teeth are some <u>recent</u> developments. But I still chew gum for the old-fashioned reasons. Gum calms a restless <u>spirit</u> and tastes like a <u>banquet</u> when you're starving. It can prevent total <u>panic</u> when you're nervous. And these days, even my dentist is happy, because I <u>presently</u> chew only <u>sugarless</u> gum!

This is Bev Windsor, signing off for Kids' Report.

Observing Patterns

1. Write the list words that name the citizens of three countries.

2. Write the two-syllable list words. From your list, circle the two words that have the stress on the second syllable.

3. Unscramble the syllables of the following list words.

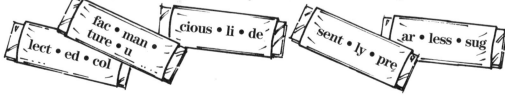

fac • man • ture • u

cious • li • de

sent • ly • pre

ar • less • sug

lect • ed • col

4. **a)** Complete each set with a list word.
fear, terror, fright, _____
podiatrist, chiropractor, optician, _____
produce, create, build, _____
feast, celebration, festivities, _____

b) Write two more sets that can be completed by list words. Try these on a partner.

Discovering Patterns

item method Canadian admit spirit presently manufacture disgrace banquet sugarless collected delicious panic recent syrup American dentist Mexican

1. Say these words.

item   method   syrup   present   recent

Listen to the vowel sound in the stressed syllable. Can you hear it clearly? Now listen to the vowel sound in the unstressed syllable. Is this vowel easy to identify?

Many vowels in unstressed syllables are **schwa vowels** /ə/. No matter how they are spelled, they all sound somewhat the same. With **schwa vowels**, we must learn other ways to remember the spelling.

2. Think of special ways to remember the list words above.

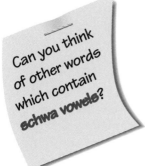

Can you think of other words which contain schwa vowels?

POWERBOOSTER

- The vowel sound in many unstressed syllables is the **schwa** sound /ə/, as in the second syllable of **item** or **method**.

94

Exploring Patterns

1. Write the list words that match the pronunciation symbols in each bubble. Pay special attention to the **schwa** vowel /ə/ in many of the words.

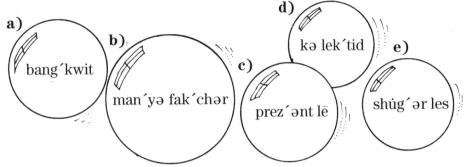

a) bang´kwit

b) man´yə fak´chər

c) prez´ənt lē

d) kə lek´tid

e) shùg´ər les

2. Match the following suffixes to the list words below. Use each suffix only once. Then write each new word in a sentence.

-ful   -ize   -ly   -less   -ual   -ry

recent　　　　disgrace　　　　item

dentist　　　　sugar　　　　　spirit

3. Design a word web for the word **banquet**. You may use any word that is connected in some way with **banquet**.

4. Many of the list words have been borrowed from other languages. Match each root word below with one of the list words. Notice that the meaning of the list word has often changed over the years.

Language	Root	Meaning	List Word
Arabic	**sharab**	*beverage or drink*	
Italian	**banco**	*a bench*	
Latin	**spiritus**	*breath, life, soul*	
Greek	**panikos**	*Pan: Greek god who could arouse terror*	
Latin	**manufacere**	*to make by hand*	

Use your dictionary for help with the meaning of new words.

5. Design a set of 'bubble gum' cards showing your favourite rock stars, sports heroes, or crazy trivia facts. Trade your cards with a friend, and proofread each other's information.

10 Sylvie Martin	CENTRE
BASKETBALL	

Height: 140 cm
Born: 06/06/84
Hometown: Winnipeg
Nickname: Hoops

Scouting Report

Most Improved Player

Challenges with Words

1. Match each Super Word to the set of words below.

   a) maple, cinnamon, _____

   b) certainly, absolutely, _____

   c) anthology, assortment, _____

   d) warranty, pledge, _____

   e) endorse, advocate, _____

2. Complete each Super Word below. Notice that many of the Super Words contain double letters and schwa vowels.

   a) g _ _ r _ nt _ _   **d)** dent _ l

   b) reco _ _ end   **e)** pe _ _ ermint

   c) def _ n _ t _ ly   **f)** c _ l _ ect _ on

3. Peppermint is a flavour used in making chewing gum. With a partner, brainstorm a list of other flavours that you could use in chewing gum. Use a dictionary to check your spelling.

SUPER WORDS

recommend
collection
dental
definitely
guarantee
peppermint

Write a recipe for making gum with your favourite flavour.

4. Many people keep a **collection** of things they are interested in, such as stamps, hockey cards, or coins. List at least three types of collections you would like to have. Choose your favourite one and describe how you might display it for others to see.

5. The Super Word **dental** is an adjective which describes something related to a dentist. Do you know these other adjectives?

    a) A <u>doctor</u> has a _____ practice.
    b) A <u>musician</u> is a _____ person.
    c) A <u>lawyer</u> signs _____ papers.

6. Design a full-page ad for a new, super-tasting chewing gum. Use all the Super Words in your ad.

Does **your** chewing gum loose its flavour after weeks of chewing?

Try _____ !

Schwa Vowels

vital   multiply

pirate
office
purchase
funds
history
vital
multiply
valuable
credit
personal
standard
coins
exchange
manager
currency
private
balance
capital

Cattle into Plastic Cards

This is Nigel DeBarlo with a Kids' Report feature on the history of money.

There's an old saying 'A penny saved is a penny earned.' At one time, there were no pennies. If you needed something vital, you traded, or bartered for it. Eventually, objects such as animal hides or tea were used as a standard of exchange. Cattle were often used. Our word for money, capital, comes from the Latin *caput*, meaning 'a head (of cattle)'. Not only were cows valuable, they could also multiply in number!

Later, coins made of gold and silver became popular as currency. These metals were used for personal adornment, and didn't rust. A pirate who buried gold coins could be sure they would still be precious when he dug them up.

These days, people can use credit cards to purchase many items, without any money changing hands. That's all done by the bank. Of course, it's still important to be a good money manager and to balance your bank account. Otherwise, as the saying goes, 'No funds, no fun!'

Observing Patterns

1. Write the list words that would be found in the dictionary between **camera/purse**.

2. Write the list words that match these shapes.

3. Write the list words that mean the opposite of the following:

sell   worthless   public   unnecessary

Discovering Patterns

pirate office purchase funds history vital multiply valuable credit personal standard coins exchange manager currency private balance capital

1. a) Write these list words.

president   excellent   capital   personal

The second or third syllable in each of these words is unstressed. The vowel in the unstressed syllable is known as the **schwa vowel** /ə/.

b) Circle the **schwa vowel** in both syllables of each word.

Example: *pres(i)d(e)nt*

You will notice that although the schwa vowel sounds almost the same in each word, it is spelled with four different letters: **a**, **e**, **i**, **o**. For this reason, unstressed syllables require special attention.

2. Remember this important principle in spelling: words which are related in meaning are usually related in spelling.

If you are unsure of how to spell a word, think of other forms of the word. It is easy to remember the silent **g** in **sign** if you think of **signal**.

Example: *si**g**n—si**g**nal*

If the difficult part of a word is a schwa vowel in an unstressed syllable, such as in comp**o**sition, think of a form of the word where the vowel is not a schwa, such as in **compose**.

/ə/—Why do we use an upside down *e* for schwa? Maybe because it's no particular vowel sound.

POWERBOOSTER

- Special attention must be paid to the spelling of many unstressed syllables, since the vowel sound, known as a schwa sound /ə/, is not clearly pronounced.

Exploring Patterns

1. Write the words that match each set of pronunciation symbols below. One word in each pair is a list word.

    a) his´tə rē   his tô´rik

    b) vī´təl   vī tal´ə tē

2. a) The first word in each pair above has a **schwa vowel** in the second syllable. Write each of these words and circle the letter which spells the schwa vowel.

Example: *opp*ⓞ*site*

    b) Now say the second word in each pair and notice how the vowel in the second syllable is easy to hear. Circle the vowel in the second syllable. Remembering the related word will help you to spell these list words.

3. Complete each analogy below.

    a) A **pirate** is like a **bank robber** because _____ .
       A **pirate** is different than a **bank robber** because _____ .
    b) **History** is like an **adventure story** because _____ .
       History is different than an **adventure story** because _____ .

4. Complete the list words on each coin. Pay special attention to the spelling of those with schwa vowels.

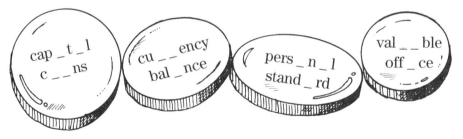

cap _ t _ l
c _ _ ns

cu _ _ ency
bal _ nce

pers _ n _ l
stand _ rd

val _ _ ble
off _ ce

5. Many idioms in English involve the topic of money. Rewrite each sentence so that it could be understood by someone new to the English language.

    a) Money burns a hole in your pocket.
    b) I certainly got short-changed on that deal.
    c) You look like a million dollars!
    d) If you buy a bike from him, you'll pay through the nose.
    e) A penny for your thoughts?

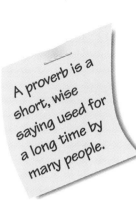

A proverb is a short, wise saying used for a long time by many people.

finance
depositing
decimal
estimate
monetary
speculate

6. Here are some proverbs about money.

Money is the root of all evil.
See a penny, pick it up—all that day you'll have good luck.
A penny saved is a penny earned.

Choose one of the proverbs above, and write your opinion explaining why you think it is true, or <u>not</u> true.

7. Write a saying of your own about money. You can use some of the proverbs above to get you started. Try to pack as much meaning as you can into as few words as possible.

Example: '*See a penny, pick it up, and pretty soon you'll have heavy pockets.*'

Challenges with Words

1. Write the Super Words that fit the blanks.

Analysts Ponder Big Bucks' Future

Canadian m_____ experts are uncertain how a multi-million dollar error might affect Big Bucks International, the megacorporation. Yesterday, while _____ some large cheques, a company employee accidentally put the _____ point in the wrong place. Experts _____ that a mistake involving several millions may have been made. A conservative _____ is that Big Bucks may have lost one million dollars, money which was to have been used to _____ a new development in St. John's.

2. Write your own paragraph with blanks for the Super Words. Trade it with a partner.

━━━━━ **WORDS IN HISTORY** ━━━━━

<u>Decem</u> is a Latin word which means 'ten'. The Super Word **decimal** comes from the adjective form, <u>decimus</u>, which was used as a person's name and meant 'the tenth-born in a family'.

3. Spelling Investments: The /ə/ sound often makes it difficult to spell a word correctly. Write the words below from their phonetic spelling.

     a) kal´ən dər   _ _ _ _ _ _ _ _
     b) tri men´dəs   _ _ _ _ _ _ _ _ _ _
     c) luk´shə rē   _ _ _ _ _ _
     d) rek´ə mend´   _ _ _ _ _ _ _ _ _

4. **Monetary** is an adjective which means 'having to do with money'. In Canada, the **monetary** unit is the **dollar**. Match these other monetary units with the countries to which they belong.

Monetary Units		Countries	
drachma	lira	Denmark	China
pound sterling	krona	Mexico	Italy
peseta	franc	Saudi Arabia	Spain
riyal	yuan	England	Greece
krone	peso	Sweden	France

5. There are many monthly newsletters which advise people on making financial decisions. Write a one-page newsletter advising people how to invest their money. Use as many Super Words as you can. You might start your newsletter like the example below.

NEW WORDS

ATM
bank card
calling card

6. New ways of banking and paying for things are developing all the time. Match the new words to these clues.

a) Which card do you use to make a long distance phone call, or call home collect? _____

b) What is the acronym for Automated Teller Machine? _____

c) Which card do you use to withdraw cash and make deposits? _____

Final Unstressed Syllables

awful stolen

total
dazzle
diamond
mineral
dollar
glitter
awful
farther
nickel
crystal
original
brilliant
tunnel
billion
stolen
emerald
double
polish

Rocks into Jewellery

This is Amy Wong for Kids' Report, at a <u>diamond</u> mine in South Africa. Here, people <u>tunnel</u> deep into the ground for this most valuable <u>mineral</u> on Earth. Someday, they may discover a <u>billion dollar</u> diamond. Many famous diamonds are worth millions. One of the largest, the 'Orloff Diamond,' was <u>stolen</u> by a French soldier from a temple in India. The 189 carat gem travelled <u>farther</u> and farther from India until today, it has become part of the Russian crown jewel collection.

A diamond, like an <u>emerald</u> or ruby, is precious because it is rare. But diamonds have a <u>double</u> value. A diamond is a <u>crystal</u>, ninety times harder than corundum, the next hardest substance on Earth. Only another diamond can cut it, and it can be burned only at temperatures of over 2760°C. This makes diamonds important in many industries. A diamond drill penetrates solid rock, searching for minerals such as gold and <u>nickel</u>. It may also be a diamond drill that makes that <u>awful</u> noise in the dentists' office!

In its <u>original</u> state, a diamond doesn't <u>glitter</u> and sparkle. It's the cut and <u>polish</u> of the stone that allow it to <u>dazzle</u> our eyes. The most common diamond shape is the <u>brilliant</u> cut, a stone with a <u>total</u> of 58 facets or faces.

This is Amy Wong, digging in for Kids' Report.

Observing Patterns

1. Write the list words that match these shapes.

103

2. Write the list words that fit the following clues. Then add one other word that you know for each clue.

  a) contains the sound /o/ as in **mop** spelled **aw**
  b) contains the sound /j/ as in **jeep** spelled **g**
  c) contains the sound /i/ as in **trip** spelled **y**
  d) contains the sound /u/ as in **rub** spelled **ou**
  e) contains the sound /k/ as in **can** spelled **ck**

3. Write the list words that fit the following definitions.

  a) the sum of all the parts
  b) any substance obtained by mining
  c) at a greater distance
  d) a colourless or tinted precious stone, formed of pure carbon in crystals
  e) a bright green, precious stone

4. Write the list words that contain **double consonants**. Circle the double consonants.

Discovering Patterns

total dazzle diamond mineral dollar glitter awful farther nickel crystal original brilliant tunnel billion stolen emerald double polish

1. Write the following list words.

  awful   double   nickel   crystal

Each of these words ends in the **schwa** sound + **l** /əl/. Circle the letters that spell the /əl/ sound in each word.

2. Write the following words.

  dollar   farther   glitter   doctor

Each of these words ends in the schwa sound + **r** /ər/. Circle the letters that spell the /ər/ sound in each word.

Can you think of special memory tricks to remember
• the **o** in doctor
• the **a** in dollar?

POWERBOOSTER

- Many English words contain a **schwa vowel** in the final syllable. These words deserve special attention, because the **schwa** sound is difficult to hear.

Exploring Patterns

1. The **schwa** endings of list words have been cut off in these 'single cut' diamonds. Combine the **schwa** endings on the outer rings with the word parts in the middle to form list words. Use each word part only once.

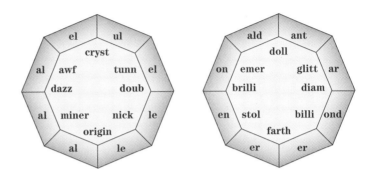

2. Explain in your own words what is meant by each of the following proverbs and expressions.
   a) I can easily **polish** off a litre of milk in one meal.
   b) All that **glitters** is not gold.
   c) Your message is **crystal** clear.
   d) Don't take any wooden **nickels**!

3. a) Read the dictionary entry below for the word diamond.

   dia•mond [dī´mənd *or* di´ə mənd]   **1** a colourless or tinted precious stone formed of pure carbon in crystals. **2** a figure shaped like this ◆. **3** a playing card having one or more red, diamond-shaped designs on it. **4** in baseball, the space inside the lines that connect the bases.

   b) Write the number of the definition above that fits each sentence below.

   The magician drew a ten of diamonds from the deck of cards.
   The ring contained a cluster of diamonds.
   The baseball diamond was soaked by the rain.
   The swimming pool was diamond shaped.

4. Replace each underlined word with a list word.
   a) We decided to <u>burrow</u> our way through the snow bank.
   b) The <u>real</u> painting is in a museum, but we have a reproduction of it.
   c) A ten-dollar bill is worth <u>twice</u> the value of a five.
   d) Be sure to <u>shine</u> your shoes before the presentation.

105

5. **a)** Suppose you open a prize in a bag of potato chips and discover a diamond ring. You know it's real because it can cut glass. With a partner, brainstorm a series of events that might follow this amazing discovery.

b) Write a short story based on these events. Compare your story with your partner's and see how each of you used the ideas.

Challenges with Words

1. Match the correct Super Word to the clues below.
   a) a kind of twin
   b) an eight-sided, geometric solid
   c) a homophone for something a rabbit might eat
   d) an antonym for **weak**
   e) a side of b)
   f) a pair of train tracks is one example

2. **a)** The Super Word **carat** is a difficult word to remember because it belongs to a family of four homophones! Match these homophones to their correct meanings. Use a dictionary to check your answers.

carat	a mark (∧) in proofreading
karat	a unit of mass for precious stones
caret	a vegetable
carrot	measure of the purity of gold

b) Use some of the homophones above to complete this limerick.

A hare, who once married for money,
Asked a ten _____ ring of his bunny.
She offered some gold
Ten _____ , I'm told,
But he settled for _____ and honey!

c) Now try writing a nonsense rhyme of your own. Use as many of these **carat** homophones as you can.

carat
invincible
identical
facet
parallel
octahedron

Use a dictionary to check your answers.

The ancient Greek word for **diamond** was <u>adamos</u>, which meant 'the invincible'. The Super Word **invincible** means the same as it did in ancient Rome, <u>invincibilis</u>, 'impossible to destroy'.

3. Diamonds are natural **octahedrons**. How many sides or **facets** does a diamond have?

4. Do you know other geometric terms? Use the clues to fill in the missing letters below.

a) a five-sided figure   _ _ _ _ _ g _ _
b) a solid that holds ice cream   _ _ _ e
c) a ten-sided polygon   _ _ _ _ _ o _
d) a four-sided solid found in Egypt   _ _ _ _ m _ _
e) a six-angled figure   _ e _ _ _ _ _
f) a three-angled figure   t _ _ _ _ _ _ _
g) a round solid   _ _ _ _ re
h) a many-angled figure   _ _ _ y _ _ _

5. a) A word or sentence which is **identical** when read forward or backward is called a **palindrome**.

Example: *noon*
           madam
           kayak
           Madam I'm Adam

           A man a plan a canal Panama!

Write five more words that are palindromes.

b) Try writing a palindrome sentence.
c) Share your palindromes with a partner to make a palindrome dictionary.

Hint! A word that means a member of a family is a palindrome.

23 Final Unstressed Syllables

fier**c**er dar**k**en mom**ent**

imagine
director
actor
theatre
instant
putty
figure
fiercer
bottles
sunken
beard
mustache
wrinkles
suggest
containers
moment
darken
title

Actor into Beast

Hi! This is Alexander Douglas, backstage at the <u>theatre</u>. The <u>title</u> of the play this week is 'Beauty and the Beast'. I'm in the make-up room watching an <u>actor</u> become a <u>beast</u>. On the table in front of us are <u>containers</u> of stage make-up, and <u>bottles</u> of hair dye.

At this <u>instant</u>, the make-up artist is applying grease paint to <u>darken</u> the actor's face. This will give the effect of <u>sunken</u> cheeks. A full <u>beard</u> and <u>mustache</u> will help <u>suggest</u> the figure of the Beast. A few <u>wrinkles</u> around the actor's eyes will make him seem older and <u>fiercer</u>. A lot of <u>putty</u> on the end of his nose will make it longer. Finally, fake fangs will be glued over his teeth. It will be easy to <u>imagine</u> that the actor is really a beast.

The <u>director</u> is calling for the actors to come onstage. In a <u>moment</u> the show will begin. This is Alexander Douglas, hurrying to my seat to watch the show.

Observing Patterns

1. Complete the following sentences with list words.
   a) At the end of the performance, the famous _____ , walked onstage, and bowed for a _____ . In an _____ , the audience was giving a standing ovation.
   b) The various _____ held make-up and dye which were used to hide _____ , and to _____ the actor's _____ , and _____ .

2. Write the list words that match the clues below.
   a) are in the plural form _____ , _____ , _____
   b) are forms of facial hair on men _____ , _____
   c) have double consonants _____ , _____ , _____
   d) contain three syllables _____ , _____ , _____ , _____

Discovering Patterns

imagine director actor theatre instant putty figure fiercer bottles sunken beard mustache wrinkles suggest containers moment darken title

1. a) Write the list words below. The final syllable of these words contains the sound /ər/.

   actor   containers   theatre   figure

   b) Circle the letters that show how the /ər/ sound is spelled in each word.

2. a) Write these list words. The final syllable contains the sound /ən/.

   imagine   sunken   darken

   b) Circle the letters that show how the /ən/ sound is spelled in each word.

3. a) Write these list words. The final syllable contains the sound /ənt/.

   moment   instant

   b) Circle the letters that show how the /ənt/ sound is spelled in each word.

4. a) Write these list words. The final syllable contains the sound /əl/.

   bottles   wrinkles   title

   b) Circle each word to show how the /əl/ sound is spelled.

POWERBOOSTER

* The final syllable of many words contains a **schwa vowel** which can be spelled in a number of ways.

Many people pronounce **figure** with yər at the end, especially when it refers to the body.

Exploring Patterns

1. Write the list word that matches the pronunciation symbol on each grease paint container. Pay special attention to the **schwa** vowels.

The schwa /ə/ is pronounced "uh".

ring´kəlz   i maj´ ən   sə jest´   bot´ əlz

2. Add each suffix in the box to one of the list words below, making changes if necessary. Then use each new word in a sentence.

| -ion   -ation   -ly   -ion |

  a) instant
  b) suggest
  c) imagine
  d) director (add suffix to base word)

3. Create a word web for **theatre**.

Example:

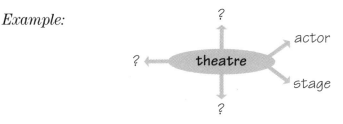

4. Combine each pair of sentences below into a single sentence. You may drop some words and add others as long as the meaning remains the same.

  a) The actor trimmed his mustache. Then he shaved off his beard.
  b) The director told the actors to stop for a moment. She told them to imagine they had just found a sunken, treasure chest.
  c) I enjoy going to the theatre. I feel that I am part of the play that is onstage.

5. a) At the left are some props an actor might use in creating a character. Choose any of them or add others, then design a disguise for yourself.
  b) Describe how you would look.
  c) What do you think would happen if you were to walk into class in your disguise?

110

competent
technique
dimple
illusion
lengthen
futile

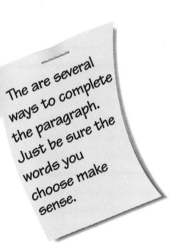

The are several ways to complete the paragraph. Just be sure the words you choose make sense.

Challenges with Words

1. Fill in the blank with a Super Word that is a synonym for the words listed below.

    a) trick, fantasy, _____
    b) method, skill, _____
    c) crease, wrinkle, _____
    d) extend, stretch, _____
    e) useless, unsuccessful, _____
    f) experienced, knowledgeable, _____

2. Look at these examples of make-up applied by a make-up artist. Write a descriptive word and a character name for each set of eyes.

Example: *sleepy—Hazel Dreamlow*

3. The Super Word **lengthen** comes from **length**. Complete the sentences in the paragraph below with the correct **-en** forms of these words.

wide	light	height	fright
tight	length	soft	short

Make-up artists have many tricks up their sleeves. They can _____ eyes that are too narrow, _____ the colour of the cheeks with rouge, and _____ harsh lines and shadows. They can _____ dark shadows, _____ sagging chins, and _____ or _____ a nose. They can even _____ you by creating a monster!

4. The ending **que** makes the sound /k/ as in **technique** /tek nēk´/. Combine the syllables below with **que** to form words which fit the clues.

        opa   bouti   uni   grotes   anti

    a) A small clothing store is a _____ .
    b) An old piece of furniture is sometimes called an _____ .
    c) Something which blocks out light is _____ .
    d) If it's one of a kind, it's _____ .
    e) Something odd or unnatural in appearance or manner is _____ .

5. An **illusion** is something that creates a false impression. Make-up creates the **illusion** of a character. Imagine you have been asked to play the part of someone who is ninety years old.

   a) What make-up and props would you use to create the **illusion** of age?

   b) Now, write a description of the part you would like to play while wearing this disguise. Will you play a hero or a villain?

World Wide Web

surfing

home page

6. The new words all have to do with the Internet. Match the new words to the clues below.

   a) to look or browse through information on the web

   b) often the first page you see when you go to a web site

   c) a very large collection of electronic publications and information

STUDY STEPS

LOOK
SAY
COVER
WRITE
CHECK

Here is a list of challenging words from Units 19–23.

banquet	original	sensitive	delicious
awful	theatre	wrinkles	dollars
mustache	diamond	brilliant	crystal
manufacture	visible	beginning	valuable
capital	syrup	forgetting	office

1. Use the Study Steps for each word. Your teacher will then dictate the words.

2. Complete the story with words from the Study List. Some of the beginning letters have been included to help you.

The other night I saw an excellent movie about the life of a famous actor. It was the o_____ version in black and white. In the b_____ , her life seemed wonderful. Every night, she went to the t_____ and wore v_____ _____s and emeralds worth thousands of d_____ . She was even invited to a b_____ in Washington, D.C., the _____ of the United States. There, she danced with the President under a dazzling, c_____ chandelier.

Sadly, her b_____ movie career came to an a_____ end. As she began f_____ her lines and became _____ about losing her fame. Soon she started to _____ excuses for missing work. Her life story was interesting, but I think my next movie will be a comedy!

3. Write the review words that match these shapes.

4. Write the review words that mean the opposite of these words.

invisible	dull	conclusion
worthless	unfeeling	tasteless

5. Complete each review word by supplying the correct vowels.

    a) _ rig _ n _ l   **b)** sens _ tive

    c) man _ fact _ re   **d)** the _ tr _

    e) di _ m _ nd   **f)** _ ff _ ce

6. Complete each sentence by adding **-ed** or **-ing** to the verbs in brackets. Make changes to the base words as needed.

    a) Our team was (win) until our best player (trip) and (sprain) her ankle. We (carry) her off the field and (wrap) a bandage around her ankle.

    b) Have you ever (wonder) why no swimming is (permit) on that beach?

    c) Are you (whisper) about the party we're (plan) for Mom?

    d) They are (begin) to enjoy (collect) stamps and (arrange) them in their albums.

7. Complete the words on the wheel spokes with the correct **schwa vowel** and **consonant**.

The words in part a) each end in the /ər/ sound as in **container**.

Those in part b) end in the /əl/ sound as in **title**.

Hint! /ər/ can be spelled or, er, re, ure, ar. /əl/ can be spelled le, al, el, ul.

a)   **b)**

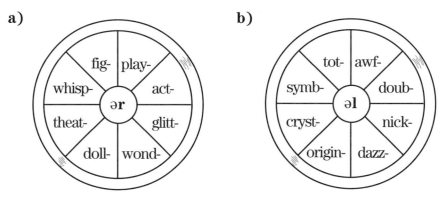

8. Work with a partner to write at least two related words for each of the following. You may write the base word, or add prefixes and suffixes.

            imagine   personal   visible

9. **a)** Create your own review list with words that were difficult for you in Units 19–23 and words from your personal word list.

    b) Construct a puzzle or exercise that will help you remember how to spell the words on your list.

Dictionary Skills

1. Primary and Secondary Stress: An entry word in a dictionary is divided into syllables. A black dot separates each syllable, as in **pro • cess**. One of the syllables is said more loudly, or with more stress than the other. An accent mark in dark type shows which syllable is stressed.

Example: *prō´ ses*

Write the words that match the dictionary pronunciations below. Place an accent after the syllable that is stressed.

(kap ə təl)   (dis grās)   (di rek tər)

Longer words may have two accented syllables. The strongest stress is called **primary stress**, and is shown by an accent mark in dark type. The lighter stress is called **secondary stress**, and is shown in lighter type.

Example: *ôr´ gə nīz´*

  a) Write the words that match the dictionary pronunciations below. Circle the syllable that has primary stress.
  b) Underline the syllable that has secondary stress.

  man´ yə fak´ chər   in´ və tā´ shən   i maj´ ə nā´ shən

2. Different Pronunciations: For some words, the dictionary gives two or more pronunciations.

Example: **whim • per** *(wim´ pər or hwim´ pər)*
        fer • tile *(fĕr´ tīl or fĕr´ təl)*

In such cases, both pronunciations are correct, but the form given first is more common across Canada as a whole. In spite of this, the second form may be more common in a certain area or with certain people.

Read the pronunciation symbols for the words below. Sound out the different pronunciations given. For each word, write the set of symbols for the pronunciations that you believe are more common in your area.

pro • cess (prō´ ses or pros´ es)
dia • mond (dī´ mənd or dī´ ə mənd)
val • u • a • ble (val´ yə bəl or val´ yü ə bəl)
his • to • ry (his´ tə rē or his´ trē)

Ask the Expert

1. Radio phone-in shows are very popular because they give people a chance to talk to the experts.

  a) Choose a topic that interests you. If you were a host on a radio talk show, what type of expert would you have on your show? Here are some examples to get you started.

Topic	Expert
Can a pet be happy living in an apartment?	vet
Is it important to take vitamins?	doctor
Is TV violence harmful to young children?	psychiatrist

Use reference books, magazines, video, or CD-ROM to help you find your answers. Or, ask an expert!

  b) List at least five questions you can ask your expert, then find out the answers to your questions.

  c) Hold a panel discussion of experts, using the questions and answers you prepared. Invite questions from your 'listening audience'.

Grammar Power

1. Conjunctions: Conjunctions are words that connect other words, phrases, or sentences. The underlined words in the following sentences are conjunctions:

> I'll clean <u>and</u> tidy my room, <u>but</u> first I need to take a nap.
> <u>When</u> you are finished, I would like to use the telephone.

Complete each of the sentences below with a conjunction from the box. Notice that when two sentences are joined by a conjunction, a comma is placed before the conjunction.

Example: *The baby is only ten months old, yet she is already walking.*

because	but	unless	and

a) _____ you have finished your homework, you will not be able to go to the movies.
b) We ordered pepper, mushrooms, _____ sausage as pizza toppings.
c) I would like to buy the tape, _____ I don't have enough money.
d) The car wouldn't start _____ the gas tank was empty.

2. Sentence Combining: Conjunctions can be used to join short, choppy sentences. Combine the pairs of sentences below with a suitable conjunction.
a) The soccer team played Saturday. They also played a game on Sunday
b) It was snowing heavily. We decided to stay home.
c) I like broccoli and spinach. I don't like fried potatoes.

Proofing Power

Read the passage below, then rewrite it correcting all the spelling errors.

Last week we visited my aunt. She is known for her great jewellery. Sure enough, she was wearing a large ring, a dimond or chrystal, worth thousands of dolers. We went to the theiter and saw an origanal play. After that we went to a banquette where the food was delishous!

The next morning we had pancakes. My aunt, forgeting that she was wearing her ring, stuck her hand in a jar of blueberry sirrop. It was hard to clean her ring. The syrrup was still visable after several washings. What an aweful thing to happen to a beautiful ring like that!

Unstressed Endings

-ant -ent -ible -able

pleas**ant** garm**ent** impos**sible** wash**able**

vegetable
garment
pleasant
president
ignorant
capable
worthless
fashion
feathers
washable
responsible
servant
comfortable
factory
excellent
wealthy
impossible
sergeant

Hats

This is Beverley Windsor for Kids' Report. What's the most important <u>garment</u> in history? The hat!

There's no doubt that a hat can change the way you look. At one time, every adult wore a hat, from humble <u>servant</u> to prime minister, or <u>president</u>. A hat <u>factory</u> was <u>capable</u> of turning out hundreds of top hats or bowler hats each day. These days, the hat market is more specialized. People wear hats to show that they are in the height of <u>fashion</u>. A <u>sergeant</u> wears a special hat to indicate his or her rank. A sailor wears a <u>washable</u> hat that won't be damaged by water.

Of course, some people will tell you that hats are <u>worthless</u>, and that it's

<u>impossible</u> to find a hat to suit them. These people may be <u>ignorant</u> of the fact that hats are <u>excellent</u> for keeping your head warm, or for throwing a <u>pleasant</u> shade when the sun is blazing. Personally, my favourite hat is this <u>comfortable</u> old thing I wear for working in my flower and <u>vegetable</u> garden. Of course, I wouldn't want my friends to see me wearing my hat— it makes me look completely different!

Observing Patterns

1. **a)** Write the six list words that have three syllables. Put an accent (´) on each stressed syllable.

    b) Write the four list words that have four syllables. Put an accent (´) on each stressed syllable.

    c) Which list word is sometimes pronounced with three syllables and sometimes with four?

Discovering Patterns

vegetable garment pleasant president ignorant capable worthless fashion feathers washable responsible servant comfortable factory excellent wealthy impossible sergeant

1. **a)** Many of the list words contain the sound /ənt/ in the final syllable, as in **present** or **tenant**. It is important to pay attention to the spelling of this syllable, since it contains a **schwa vowel**. Complete the following chart with list words that end in **-ent** or **-ant**.

/ənt/ spelled **-ent**	/ənt/ spelled **-ant**

b) Add to each column two other words you know that fit these patterns.

2. **a)** Many of the list words contain the sound /əbəl/ in the final syllables, as in **sensible** and **probable**. The **schwa vowels** make both **-ible** and **-able** sound the same. Therefore, it is important to pay special attention to the spelling of these syllables. Complete the following chart with list words that end in **-ible** or **-able**.

/əbəl/ spelled **-ible**	/əbəl/ spelled **-able**

b) Add two other words you know that fit these patterns to each column.

These words are import**ant**!

... and these are incred**ible**!

POWERBOOSTER

- The final unstressed syllable /ənt/ may be spelled **-ent**, as in **present** or **-ant**, as in **tenant**.
- The final unstressed syllables /əbəl/ may be spelled **-ible**, as in **sensible** or **-able**, as in **probable**.

Exploring Patterns

1. Complete the list words on each hat with one of the endings on the brim.

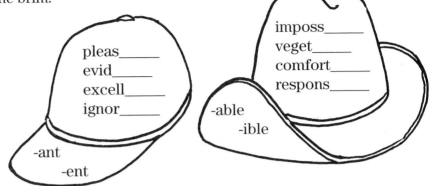

pleas_____
evid_____
excell_____
ignor_____

-ant
-ent

imposs_____
veget_____
comfort_____
respons_____

-able
-ible

2. Complete each sentence with the word in brackets which has the required number of syllables and the correct stress.

a) 4 syllables; second syllable stressed
The mountain ahead looked (challenging, impossible, reasonable) to climb.

b) 3 syllables; first syllable stressed
He received a call from the factory (owner, inspector, president).

c) 4 syllables; first syllable stressed
I bought this hat because it's (comfortable, washable, reversible).

3. a) Write the words that are represented by each set of pronunciation symbols. One word in each pair is a list word. A meaning clue is given for each word.

ig nôr´	paying no attention to	_____
ig´nə rənt	knowing little or nothing	_____
plēz	give enjoyment to	_____
plez´ənt	easy to get along with	_____
ek sel´	do better than others	_____
ek´sə lənt	first class	_____
pri zid´	hold the place of authority	_____
prez´ə dənt	the chief officer	_____

b) Remember that words which are related in meaning are usually spelled in similar ways, even if they are pronounced differently.

Circle the parts of each word pair above which are pronounced differently but spelled the same.

Example: (admir)e (admir)ation

Knowing the base word *ignore* helps spell *ignorant*.

119

4. The following expressions are idioms containing the word **hat**. Rewrite each sentence so that it would be understood by someone new to the English language.

   a) The hockey star scored a <u>hat trick</u> last night.
   b) I <u>take my hat off to you</u> for the work you've done.
   c) Let's <u>pass the hat</u> for the girl whose wallet was stolen.

5. This parent wants his six-year-old to wear a warm tuque to school. None of the other kids in his class wears a hat. Write a conversation that you imagine the father might have with his son. What kind of compromise do you think they might reach? Set up your conversation in dialogue form.

FATHER: Ivan, you have to wear this hat!
IVAN: But Dad…

Challenges with Words

1. Match the Super Words to these picture/word clues.

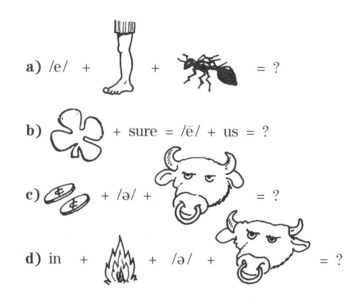

a) /e/ + + = ?

b) + sure = /ē/ + us = ?

c) + /ə/ + = ?

d) in + + /ə/ + = ?

━━━━ WORDS IN HISTORY ━━━━

The Super Word **inflammable** comes from the Latin verb <u>inflammare</u>, 'to set on fire'. Often it is spelled **flammable**, because the prefix **in-** can mean 'not'. **Inflammable** could be mistaken for **not flammable**!

2. Correct the paragraph below, using a Super Word in place of its underlined antonym.

My brother is an <u>unknown</u> lawyer. He lives in a <u>tasteless</u> apartment which is completely furnished with <u>shabby</u>, fireproof carpets. Last week he had a <u>forgettable</u> experience. There was a fire in his apartment. He is lucky he is so <u>foolish</u>. If his carpets had been <u>non-flammable</u>, his apartment might have suffered great damage.

3. a) Everyone's opinion as to what is **luxurious** is probably different. Make a word web for **luxurious** like the one in the margin.
b) Choose an item from your word web and describe it using words that tell why it is so **luxurious**.

4. Use your dictionary to find five words that use the prefix **in-**, meaning 'not'.

5. What are some of the most memorable things that have happened to you?
a) List five or more events or situations that were memorable in your life.
b) Rank them from **least** to **most** memorable.

6. There have been many children's stories written about hats; *Bartholomew Cubbins and the 500 Hats*, and *A Cat in a Hat*, to name two. Write your own short children's story about hats. If you can, illustrate it and read it to someone younger. Try to use some of the Super Words in your story.

7. The new words are names for recreational equipment and accessories. Complete each sentence below with the correct new word.
a) I bought a new _____ _____ for cycling on rough terrain.
b) _____ _____ are great for running, walking, and playing basketball.
c) I always wear my _____ _____ when I ride in a bike race.

Unstressed Endings

-ure -ic -ous

pleas**ure** trag**ic** humor**ous**

tragic

nervous

terrific

pleasure

creature

furious

humorous

failure

piano

lessons

mysterious

signature

torture

dramatic

serious

culture

domestic

curious

Sound into Music

This is Nigel DeBarlo, with a report about the <u>piano</u>. I used to be a <u>terrific</u> pianist, but my family said my playing sounded like a <u>mysterious</u> <u>creature</u> undergoing <u>torture</u>. Very <u>humorous</u>!

In a more <u>serious</u> vein, did you know that the piano is the most popular instrument in our <u>culture</u>? It is also very popular in Japan, which produces more pianos than any other country, and sells most of them in its own <u>domestic</u> market.

It's a <u>curious</u> fact that pianos are less than three hundred years old. The piano developed from the harpsichord, an older keyboard instrument. In the 19th century, composer Franz Liszt used to play his piano with such <u>furious</u>

energy that strings would snap and hammers fly during a performance. Very dramatic!

Modern pianos usually carry the <u>signature</u> of the manufacturer above the keyboard. Baldwin, Heintzman, Steinway, and Yamaha are names that have brought <u>pleasure</u> to millions through their pianos. As for me, I'm giving up my <u>lessons</u>. My family has made me <u>nervous</u> about being a <u>failure</u>. It's a <u>tragic</u> loss to the world. I could have been great!

Observing Patterns

1. Write the list words that fit the following clues.

    a) the sound /e/ as in **let** is spelled **ea** _ _ _ _ _ _ _ _

    b) the sound /ē/ as in **meet** is spelled **ea** _ _ _ _ _ _ _ _

    c) the sound /ch/ is spelled with a **t** _ _ _ _ _ _ _ _ , _ _ _ _ _ _ _ _ ,

    _ _ _ _ _ _ , _ _ _ _ _ _

    d) is in the plural form _ _ _ _ _ _ _

    e) a pair of rhyming words _ _ _ _ _ _ _ , _ _ _ _ _ _ _

2. Write the list words that share a common base word with the following. Then write the base word beside each word pair.

    a) signal   _____   _____

    b) nervousness   _____   _____

    c) pleasant   _____   _____

    d) humorist   _____   _____

    e) dramatize   _____   _____

    f) failing   _____   _____

3. Complete each analogy with a list word.

    a) import is to export as foreign is to _____

    b) humorous is to serious as calm is to _____

    c) pleased is to delighted as annoyed is to _____

Discovering Patterns

tragic nervous terrific pleasure creature furious humorous failure piano lessons mysterious signature torture dramatic serious culture domestic curious

1. The sound /ər/ in a final, unstressed syllable has many spellings, as in **mother**, **actor**, **mortar**, and **feature**. Write the list words that end in the /ər/ sound spelled **-ure**. Underline the **-ure** in each word.

2. The sound /əs/ in a final, unstressed syllable has several spellings, as in **compass**, **campus**, and **famous**. Write the list words that end in the /əs/ sound spelled **-ous**. Underline the **-ous** in each word.

3. Some of the list words end in the sound /ik/ as in **panic**. Write these words. Circle the letters that make the /ik/ sound.

POWERBOOSTER

- The sound /ər/ is sometimes spelled **-ure** in final, unstressed syllables, as in **picture**.
- The sound /əs/ is sometimes spelled **-ous** in final, unstressed syllables, as in **famous**.
- The sound /ik/ is often spelled **ic**, as in **picnic**.

Exploring Patterns

1. Unscramble the syllables on the song sheet to find words which end in **-ic**, **-ous**, **-ure**.

2. Make at least five sentences by taking a word from each column below, in any order, and adding your own ideas for column six.

Example: *The famous actor made a dramatic entrance.*

1	2	3	4	5	6
A	mysterious	creature	gave	a terrific	
That	famous	vulture	enjoyed	a helpless	
One	curious	actor	ruined	a gorgeous	
The	nervous	painter	attacked	a dramatic	
This	furious	doctor	made	a humorous	

3. Write the list word that fits each word origin below.

Comes from	Root	Meaning	List Word
Italian	pianoforte	*from soft and smooth to loud and strong*	
Latin	domesticus	*house*	_____
Latin	furiosus	*madness, rage*	_____
Greek	tragikos	*having a disastrous ending*	
Latin	misterium	*secret, hidden*	_____

Use a dictionary to find the word origins of two other list words.

124

4. Create a word web for each of the list words below. You may use any word that is connected in some way to the centre word.

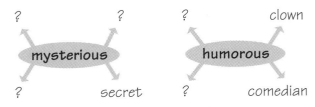

5. The **harpsichord** and the **clavichord** were ancestors of the modern piano. Do you have a favourite musical instrument? Do some research to find out more about its history and origins. Organize the information under headings such as:

- early forms of the instrument;
- how the instrument became the one we know today;
- why the instrument is important;
- why you like the instrument.

Challenges with Words

1. Match the Super Word which relates most closely in meaning to each word below. Then unscramble the circled letters to find the answer to the riddle.

a) reverberation Ⓞ_ _ _ _ _ _ _ _
b) an interval _Ⓞ_ _ _ _
c) recreation Ⓞ_Ⓞ_ _ _ _
d) desirous _Ⓞ_ _ _ _ _ _Ⓞ
e) heroic Ⓞ_Ⓞ_ _ _Ⓞ_ _ _
f) musician _ _ _ _ _Ⓞ_

Riddle: How do you weigh a piece of music?
Answer: With a _ _ _ _ _ _ _ _ _ _ .

2. Playing the piano is something some **pianists** do in their **leisure** time. Here are some other instruments that can be played during **leisure** time. Can you figure out what they are?

a) a number + the sound a sheep makes _ _ _ _
b) an exclamation + something you tie in your shoe _ _ _ _
c) a type of fish + before long _ _ _ _ _ _
d) a girl's name + where a puck goes _ _ _ _ _ _ _ _

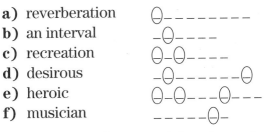

Remember to use the index of each reference book.

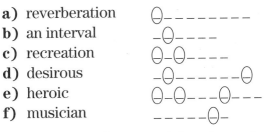

SUPER WORDS

pianist
octave
acoustics
ambitious
courageous
leisure

Notice that **leisure** is an exception to the rule 'i before e, except after c'.

125

3. **a)** An **octave** represents a certain number of notes. How many?

b) Each one of the following words stands for a **quantity** of something. Write the meaning for each word. Use your dictionary to help.

quartet   centuple   decade   duo   octogenarian

c) Now try writing two or more **quantity** words and their meanings.

4. **Take a Musical Survey:** What types of music do your friends like? Conduct a survey to find out. You might use a question sheet like the one below. Add questions of your own.

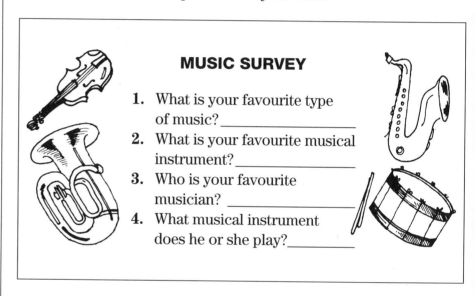

MUSIC SURVEY

1. What is your favourite type of music? _____
2. What is your favourite musical instrument? _____
3. Who is your favourite musician? _____
4. What musical instrument does he or she play? _____

27 Unstressed Endings

-age -ive -ate

st**age** impress**ive** fortun**ate**

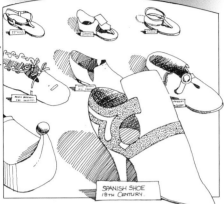

separate
positive
protective
barefoot
advantage
sandal
marriage
attractive
elaborate
average
fortunate
delicate
desperate
effective
message
impressive
detective
storage

Leather into Shoes

Hi! This is Amy Wong. In a recent Kids' Report, Beverley Windsor claimed that hats were the most important article of clothing in history. However, I'm <u>positive</u> that the <u>average</u> person would be much more upset about going <u>barefoot</u> than hatless!

Shoes have been important throughout history. In ancient Egypt, the <u>sandal</u> revealed whether a person was rich or poor. The sandals of the <u>fortunate</u> were made of silver, while those of the poor were made of leaves. The Chinese once thought tiny, <u>delicate</u> feet were very <u>attractive</u> for women. Parents tightly bound their daughters' feet in <u>elaborate</u> slippers. At some ancient <u>marriage</u> ceremonies, the

father threw shoes at the young couple to give the <u>message</u> that he was giving up his authority.

In our era, we have the <u>advantage</u> of having an <u>impressive</u> variety of shoes for many purposes. A jogger wears jogging shoes, which are the most <u>effective</u> shoes for running. A construction worker wears <u>protective</u>, steel-toed boots. Some people have so many shoes they need <u>separate</u> closets just for shoe <u>storage</u>. As they say, "If the shoe fits— wear it."

SPANISH SHOE 18TH CENTURY.

Observing Patterns

1. Write the list words that are similar in meaning to the following:
   a) investigator _____ **b)** lucky _____
   c) apart _____ **d)** benefit _____
   e) pleasing _____ **f)** ordinary _____

2. Write the list words that contain **double consonants**. Circle the double consonants.

3. Write the list words that rhyme with the following:
   a) handle _____
   b) porridge _____
   c) carriage _____
   d) protective _____

4. Complete each analogy with a list word.
   a) **bad** is to **good** as **negative** is to _____
   b) **strong** is to **durable** as **fragile** is to _____
   c) **winter** is to **boot** as **summer** is to _____

Discovering Patterns

separate positive protective barefoot
advantage sandal marriage
attractive elaborate average
fortunate delicate desperate effective
message impressive detective storage

1. Some of the list words have the sound /ij/ in the final, unstressed syllable, as in **hostage**. Write these words. Circle the letters which spell the /ij/ sound in each word.

2. Write the list words which have the sound /iv/ in the final, unstressed syllable, as in **negative**. Circle the letters which spell the /iv/ sound.

3. Write the list words which have the sound /it/ in the final, unstressed syllable, as in **delicate**. Circle the letters which spell the /it/ sound.

POWERBOOSTER

- The sound /ij/ in a final, unstressed syllable is often spelled **-age**, as in **hostage**.
- The sound /iv/ in a final, unstressed syllable is often spelled **-ive**, as in **negative**.
- The sound /it/ in a final, unstressed syllable is often spelled **-ate**, as in **delicate**.

128

Exploring Patterns

1. Write the list word that matches each pronunciation symbol below. Pay special attention to **double consonants** and **schwa vowels**.

mar´ij   ə trak´tiv   des´pə rit   del´ə kit   poz´ə tiv

2. The prefixes **un-**, **dis-**, and **in-** can be added to words to make them mean the opposite of the original word. Add one of these prefixes to the list words below. Then use each word formed in a sentence.

attractive   advantage   fortunate   effective   impressive

3. The following idioms relate to **shoes**. Rewrite each sentence so that the meaning of the underlined expression is clear.

- **a)** It will be difficult to <u>fill your shoes</u> after you leave.
- **b)** I'm glad I'm not <u>in his shoes</u> right now.
- **c)** If you want to understand her, <u>walk in her shoes</u> awhile.

4. Complete the puzzle with words ending in **-ive**.

							i	v	e	noteworthy; makes an impression
							i	v	e	works well; produces an effect
							i	v	e	capable of exploding
							i	v	e	fond of talking
							i	v	e	productive; has the power to create
							i	v	e	big and heavy; having great mass
							i	v	e	moving much or quickly
							i	v	e	person born in a certain place or country

5. Conduct some market research into shoes. With your group, determine the questions you want to ask.

Example:
- *Where do you like to buy your shoes?*
- *What is your favourite style of shoes?*
- *Do you choose your own shoes, or does someone else?*

Then, set up a questionnaire. Make it easy to read and fill in. You might survey members of your class, other groups in the school, or family members. Summarize the results of your survey in a report that would be useful to a shoe company.

Do you know other 'shoe' idioms?

Hint! Two of the answers are list words.

SUPER WORDS

moccasins
luggage
informal
soles
aggressive
ornate

thongs
loafers
clogs
sandals
sneakers

Challenges with Words

1. **a)** Rajiv is a shoe salesperson. Use the Super Words to complete this entry from his daily diary.

   My first day selling shoes at The Big Bargain Barn wasn't a very good one. Maybe I just wasn't _____ enough. First, there was the man who said he was looking for something to wear to a barbecue. I showed him a pair of _____ , but he said they were too _____ and walked away. Then, there was the lady who wanted shoes for a dinner party. I showed her a pair with silver high heels, but she said they were too _____ . And then, there was the family who wanted shoes with soft _____ for walking. They complained that every shoe I showed them wasn't big enough. Finally, I suggested they try the _____ department, and they left in a huff. I hope I have a better day tomorrow.

   b) Describe Rajiv's second day of work. Does he have a better day or not? Tell why.

   ━━━━━━━━━━━ **WORDS IN HISTORY** ━━━━━━━━━━━

   Moccasin is an Algonquian word which originally described a slipper made of deerskin or other soft leather.

2. **a) Try your feet in some of these shoes.** Match the definitions with the shoe names in the box.

   - light cloth shoes with rubber soles
   - shoes which slip on without laces
   - open shoes with straps to keep the foot in place
   - shoes with wooden soles
   - sandals held on by a toe strap

   b) Can you think of three more types of shoes?

3. **a) Soles** are something you find on the bottom of shoes. Do you know what the homophone of this word is?

   b) Now try writing some of these homophones. The meaning for each answer is given in brackets.

   frank (French money)
   attendance (escorts)
   gorilla (irregular soldier)
   style (gate)
   patients (composure)

4. Some words, such as **elaborate** and **separate**, have two pronunciations, depending on whether the word is used as a **verb** (i lab´ə rāt´) or an **adjective** (i lab´ə rit).

Write the correct ending sound for these **-ate** words (either /āt/ as in m**ate** or /it/ as in s**it**.)

   a) They will both <u>graduate</u> next year.

   b) Sportco Ltd. gave us the lowest <u>estimate</u> for our team's hockey skates.

   c) Brown and <u>Associates</u> have been hired to design a school flag.

   d) The reporter asked the speaker to <u>elaborate</u>.

5. All the new words are related to music. Some have been around for a long time, but are now more commonly used.

   a) a new type of instrumental music

   b) something you can do on a door

   c) to add a language or sound to the sound track of a film

rap

dub

new age

28

Endings
-tion -ition -ation

affec**tion** compet**ition**
starv**ation**

concentration
competition
industry
combination
affection
ingredients
chocolate
cocoa
connection
plantation
edible
addition
introduction
admiration
instruction
contribution
condition
starvation

Beans into Chocolate

This is Alexander Douglas speaking to you from a cacao <u>plantation</u> in Brazil. It's hard to make the <u>connection</u> between this strange-looking cacao tree and my favourite food— <u>chocolate</u>. The cacao beans aren't <u>edible</u> until they have been processed to produce <u>cocoa</u> powder and chocolate. Cocoa is very bitter, while the <u>addition</u> of sugar and other <u>ingredients</u> creates the chocolate flavour we know.

Since its <u>introduction</u> to Europe in 1520, chocolate has won the <u>affection</u> and <u>admiration</u> of queens and kings, as well as plenty of ordinary people, such as me! The Mexicans use it in <u>combination</u> with hot peppers as a sauce for chicken. In the last century, it was advertised as a medicine, with the <u>instruction</u> to drink a cup of hot chocolate three times a day.

The chocolate <u>industry</u> has made a great <u>contribution</u> to our lives. We consume millions of tonnes of it each year. Although you can't stay in top <u>condition</u> if you eat too much chocolate, its high <u>concentration</u> of sugar provides quick energy, and has probably prevented <u>starvation</u> on many a long, mountaineering expedition.

This is Alexander Douglas signing off for Kids' Report.

Observing Patterns

1. Write the seven four-syllable list words. Put an accent (´) on the syllable that has the greatest stress.

2. Write four three-syllable list words. Put an accent (´) on the syllable that has the greatest stress.

3. Write the list words that have double consonants. Circle the double consonants.

4. Complete each sentence with list words. Write the sentence.

a) After an hour of skating, I love to come home and mix warm milk, _____ , and sugar to make hot _____ .

b) After the storm, the owner of the cacao _____ found his crop in poor _____ .

Discovering Patterns

concentration competition industry combination affection ingredients chocolate cocoa connection plantation edible addition introduction admiration instruction contribution condition starvation

1. Many of the list words have a final syllable with the sound /shən/. The letters **-tion**, **-ation**, or **-ition** have been added to the base word.

a) Write the following list words.

connection   instruction

Beside each, write the base word. What letter is dropped when **-tion** is added to the base word?

b) Write the following list words.

introduction   production
concentration   contribution

Beside each, write the base word. What letter is dropped when **-tion** is added to the base word?

2. Write the following list words.

admiration   combination

Beside each, write the base word. What letter is dropped when **-ation** is added to the base word?

3. Write the following list words.

addition   competition

Beside each, write the base word. What letter is dropped when **-ition** is added to the base word in **competition**?

POWERBOOSTER

- When a base word ends in **silent e**, drop the **e** before adding **-tion**, **-ation**, or **-ition**.

Exploring Patterns

1. Complete this passage with list words. Some of the beginning letters have been included for you.

When we were asked to make a c_____ to the Home and School bake sale, I decided to make some _____ brownies. It was my first try, so I read the _____s on the recipe carefully. I found all the _____ and got to work. Just after the a_____ of the cocoa , the phone rang and I had a chat with my friend, Andy. I guess my _____ was broken, because I somehow forgot to add sugar to the c_____ in the bowl. When the brownies were baked, they looked great, but they tasted so bitter they weren't even _____ ! My i_____ to the joys of baking taught me one thing—unplug the phone before you begin!

2. a) Write the following list words.

**admiration   competition   production
combination   introduction**

Beside each word write the base word.
b) Circle the parts of each word pair above which are pronounced differently but spelled the same.

Example: ⟨resid⟩e / ⟨resid⟩ent

Remember: Whenever you have trouble recalling the **e** in **competition** or the **i** in **combination**, just think of the base word where the vowel is easy to hear.

3. Add **-tion**, **-ition**, or **-ation** to each verb below to create a noun. Use each word formed in a sentence.

inspect   reject   compose   invent   reserve

Example: *reduce/reduction*
We were given a reduction in price.

4. Create a word web for each of these list words below. You may use any word that is connected in some way with each centre word.

chocolate   competition

5. Design a bumper sticker for chocolate lovers. You might use your word web to help you. Bumper stickers should

- express a whole idea in a few words.
- be funny.
- be easy to remember.

SUPER WORDS

procedure
production
explanation
confection
repetition
innovation

Challenges with Words

1. Find the base word for five of the Super Words and complete the chart below. Choose one letter from each column pair.

Example: **o** i z **t**   omit   omission
          t **m** **i** s

								Base Word	Super Word
a) p	n	c	o	e	r	t	e	?	?
i	x	n	l	v	a	c	d		
b) e	x	c	l	e	u	n		?	?
b	y	p	r	a	i	t			
c) p	n	l	a	u	c	n		?	?
i	r	o	d	t	i	e			
d) r	r	p	a	e	n	t		?	?
p	x	o	c	d	e	d			
e) r	x	p	i	a	t			?	?
e	e	l	e	c	n				

══ WORDS IN HISTORY ══

Confection comes from the Latin verb, <u>conficere</u>, 'to prepare or put together'. It usually refers to something sweet, like chocolate or taffy.

2. a) List **three** of your favourite **confections**.

b) Choose one confection from your list and write down the first **five** words that it makes you think of.

c) Prepare a 'Profile of Clues' for your confection, using as many of your five words as you can. Have a partner try to guess what the confection is.

Clues

1. It's eaten after dinner.

2. It makes your breath sweet.

3. It may be hard or soft.

3. Combine one or more of the syllables in the box with **-tion** to match the meanings below. Use each syllable only once.

cel	i	quo	bi	na	lu	am	ed	ca		
med	ci	can	hal	ta	ca	u	la		+	-tion

a) a strong desire for fame or honour _____
b) what you receive in school _____
c) the sight of something which isn't really there _____
d) something a doctor prescribes _____
e) the actual words spoken _____
f) putting an end to something _____

4. The Super Word **procedure** describes a method for doing things. Choose one of the activities below (or make up your own) and outline your **procedure** for doing it.

a) getting to school on time
b) choosing the best team captain
c) running a birthday party for a six-year-old child
d) becoming the most helpful person in your neighbourhood

29 Ending -sion

tension

scientists
molten
invasion
explosion
erosion
tension
dimension
crater
conclusion
collision
confusion
destroy
earthquake
emission
erupt
fragments
lava
profession

Mountains into Volcanoes

This is Beverley Windsor standing at the foot of Mount St. Helens in the state of Washington, U.S.

In 1980, this volcano blew its top in a tremendous explosion, hurling fragments of rock and molten lava from its crater, and sending clouds of dust and gas 19 kilometres into the atmosphere. The volcano demonstrated its power to destroy anything in its path. The blast levelled a forest area with a dimension of 180 square kilometres. The emission of tonnes of volcanic ash and debris covered an even larger area.

There is still some confusion among the scientific profession about exactly why volcanoes erupt. However, scientists are coming to the conclusion that the same forces which create an earthquake, are also at work when a volcano blows its top. The theory is that Earth's crust is made up of huge plates, floating on a denser layer of crust. When a collision occurs between two such plates, it causes violent movements on Earth's surface, such as volcanic eruptions. Scientists carefully monitor the tension building up in Earth's crust.

In the meantime erosion, vegetation, and time have already begun to erase the evidence of Mt. St. Helen's amazing invasion of the surrounding area.

Observing Patterns

1. Write the list words that share the same base as the words below.

confusing   erosive   professor
explosive   concluding   invaders
intense

2. Write the list words that fit the following clues:
   a) contain double consonants _____ , _____ , _____
   b) are in the plural form _____ , _____
   c) is a compound word _____
   d) has two syllables _____

3. Complete each set with a list word.
   a) pieces, parts, bits, _____
   b) tornado, hurricane, flood, _____
   c) measurement, size, extent, _____

Discovering Patterns

scientists molten invasion explosion erosion tension dimension crater conclusion collision confusion destroy earthquake emission erupt fragments lava profession

1. a) The ending /shən/ may also be spelled **-sion**. Write the following list words.

   fusion   tension

   Beside each write the base word. What letters are dropped when adding **-sion** to base words ending in **s** and **silent e**?
   b) Add two more words that you know which follow this pattern.

2. a) Write the following list words.

   erosion   conclusion   invasion   explosion   collision

   Write the base word beside each. What letters are dropped when adding **-sion** to base words ending in **d** and **silent e**?
   b) Add two more words that you know which follow this pattern.

POWERBOOSTER

- The ending /shən/ is sometimes spelled **-sion**.
- When adding **-sion** to base words ending in **se**, drop the **se**, as in **tense/tension**.
- When adding **-sion** to base words ending in **de**, drop the **de**, as in **conclude/conclusion**.

Exploring Patterns

1. The **-sion** ending has been 'blown off' each of these words so that only the base word remains. Put back the **-sion** ending, making any necessary changes to the base word.

emit collide

fuse explode tense

erode conclude

invade

Remember to add a comma when you join two sentences with **and** or **but.**

2. Combine each set of sentences into a single sentence. You may drop words which are no longer needed, and add other words.

a) The earthquake destroyed hundreds of homes. It killed at least thirty people.

b) The volcano erupted. Molten lava poured down the mountainside.

c) It is dangerous to go near the crater's edge. This volcano is still active.

3. Complete the second sentence in each pair below by adding **-sion** to the underlined verb in the first sentence.

a) I would like to <u>discuss</u> an idea with you. A _____ would be very helpful.

b) Are you trying to <u>impress</u> me with your actions? If so, you're not making a very good _____ .

c) The robber decided to <u>confess</u> his crimes. He made his _____ to the police investigator.

d) I always wanted to <u>possess</u> my own radio. It would become my favourite _____ .

4. How many smaller words can you make by reshuffling the letters of **earthquake**? You should be able to find at least a dozen words.

5. DISASTER! Imagine you are a reporter at the scene of the Mount St. Helens eruption in the State of Washington, U.S. Write a factual report of what you see and hear. You might interview an eyewitness to the eruption. Use the report at the beginning of the unit, reference books, CD-ROMs, magazines, and newspapers to help you find information about the 1980 disaster.

Challenges with Words

1. Match a Super Word to the clues below. Each clue is an example of the Super Word, not necessarily its meaning.

- **a)** a metal alloy
- **b)** a quotient of
- **c)** your birthday
- **d)** granite
- **e)** a kitchen compared to a lawn
- **f)** automobile springs

2. Igneous rock is formed when molten rock becomes solid. Granite is perhaps the most common form of **igneous** rock. Use your dictionary or a book on geology to determine which of the following rocks are igneous.

limestone   porphyry   basalt   shale

SUPER WORDS

suspension
division
fusion
igneous
interior
occasion

| cellar |
| hold |
| scullery |
| pantry |
| corridor |

3. The inside of something is considered its **interior**. See if you can guess some of these not-so-common **interiors**. Choose a word from the box which fits each definition below. The circled letters will answer the riddle below.

   a) interior of a ship below the deck _ _ ◯ _
   b) a small room used to store food _ ◯ ◯ _ _ ◯
   c) a long hallway _ _ _ _ _ ◯ _ _
   d) a British word for a small room where the dirty work of a kitchen is done _ _ ◯ _ _ _ _ _
   e) another word for basement _ _ _ _ _ ◯

Riddle: Where are clothes washed?
Answer: _ _ _ _ _ _ _

4. a) The suffix **-sion** can have two sounds, /shən/ as in **tension**, and /zhən/ as in **confusion**. Group the **-sion** Super Words using the chart below.

-shən	**-zhən**

b) Add three more words to each **-sion** sound.

5. Brain-teaser: The is one of the ten most common words in the English language. Can you name the other nine? Here are all the letters you will need to write the words. Use each of them as many times as you like.

a d e f h i n o s t

6. New words enter our language from other countries quite often. All of these words describe dough folded over in a half-circle, with some kind of delicious filling. Match each kind of food to its culture.

   a) samosas   Caribbean
   b) patties   Ukrainian
   c) perogies   Indian

samosas

patties

perogies

141

STUDY STEPS

LOOK
SAY
COVER
WRITE
CHECK

Use each review word only once.

Here is a list of challenging words from Units 25–29.

competition	president	mysterious	destroy
desperate	sergeant	cocoa	creature
marriage	ingredients	pleasant	terrific
chocolate	separate	positive	vegetable
excellent	impossible	conclusion	attractive

1. Use the Study Steps for each word. Your teacher will then dictate the words.

2. Complete each passage with review words. The beginning letters of each missing word have been given for you.

a) All of the c_____ cakes and brownies in the baking c_____ were of e_____ quality. They contained many interesting i_____ besides the usual c_____ . I had the p_____ job of helping to judge the entries. After eating several brownies and pieces of cake, we came to the c_____ that it would be i_____ to choose just one winner. Therefore, we gave everyone an a_____ first place ribbon!

b) I read a t_____ science fiction book last week about a m_____ force that was trying to d_____ our planet. The force turned out to be a huge c_____ that ate every v_____ and fruit in sight. The world governments were becoming d_____ because there was little food left. The p_____ of the World Confederation sent armies on three s_____ occasions, but no one could stop the hungry creature.

Finally, a s_____ had an idea he was p_____ would work. He sprayed a sleeping potion on a huge pile of vegetables, and when the creature ate them, it drifted into a peaceful sleep. It was loaded onto the nearest space ship and sent deep into outer space—a happy ending to the story!

3. Write the review words that match these shapes.

|ı|ıı|ılı|ı ıı|ı|ıllı|ıl| ıı|ıl|ılıl|ıı|

4. Complete these review words. Pay special attention to the **schwa vowels**.

a) marr _ _ ge   **b)** s _ rg _ _ nt
c) pos _ tive   **d)** coc _ _
e) desp _ r _ te   **f)** sep _ r _ te
g) impo _ _ _ ble   **h)** ex _ el _ _ nt

5. a) Write the review words that are related to the following words.

please   mystery   conclude   attract   preside   terror

b) Add one more form of the word to each.

6. Add an ending from one of the smaller boxes to each base word in the centre, making changes to the base word where necessary. Use each word you have formed in a sentence.

-ant	response serve		-ent
-able	ignore comfort wash excel		-ible

7. Complete each sentence by adding one of the following endings to each underlined word part.

-ure   -ic   -ous   -age   -ive   -ate

a) The bank called in a <u>detect</u>_____ when a <u>nerv</u>_____ customer tried to forge a <u>signat</u>_____ .
b) It was a real <u>pleas</u>_____ reading this <u>impress</u>_____ collection of short stories. Some of the stories are very <u>humor</u>_____ , others are <u>seri</u>_____ , and a few even have <u>trag</u>_____ endings.
c) It's <u>fortun</u>_____ that I received your message about putting a <u>protect</u>_____ sheet over the <u>delic</u>_____ flowers. Had they been damaged by the frost, our clients would have been <u>furi</u>_____ .

8. Add **-tion, -ition, -ation,** or **-sion**, to the base words on the outer circle. Make changes to the base word where necessary.

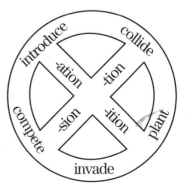

Use a dictionary to check your spellings.

Dictionary Skills

1. Idioms: An **idiom** is a phrase or expression whose meaning cannot be understood from the ordinary meanings of its individual words. For example, 'I have caught a cold' is an idiom because the expression is not understood simply by knowing the meaning of the words **caught** and **cold**. If you wish to know the meaning of an unfamiliar idiom, look up its most important word in the dictionary. Idioms are located at the end of the dictionary entry.

Read the definitions below for three idioms containing **feather.** Then match the definition with the sentence in which the idiom is used.

- something to be proud of _____
- to get rich _____
- in very good humour _____

    a) He <u>feathered his nest</u> with profits from selling stock.

    b) We were <u>in fine feather</u> on the first day of summer vacation.

    c) The successful bike-a-thon is a real <u>feather in your cap</u>.

2. Read the idioms in the box below. Then complete each sentence with one of the idioms.

in competition with	take advantage of
in connection with	on an average

    a) Be sure to _____ this once-in-a-lifetime offer!

    b) We go to a movie _____ of once a month.

    c) The suspect was questioned _____ several recent break-ins.

    d) Our skaters found themselves _____ many talented competitors.

3. Replace the underlined word or phrase in each sentence with an idiom from the box below.

in conclusion	in addition to
on condition that	to advantage

    a) I would like to purchase a pair of jeans <u>as well</u> as the sweater.

    b) My parents say I can go <u>if</u> I'm home before dinner.

    c) The speed skater used the wind <u>to her benefit</u>.

    d) <u>To summarize</u>, pollution is of concern to us all.

4. Write the idiom that is represented by each of these pictures.

a)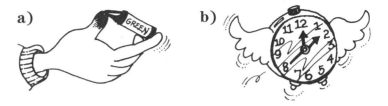

b)

...And Now for the Evening News

1. While newspapers are able to report on stories in detail, TV news programs are more limited in length. Programs are usually only thirty or sixty minutes long. They are too short to cover every important news story in detail.

  a) If you were a TV news director, how would you organize your program? List the general topics you might have. For example: national news, local news, sports, and so on.
  b) For each topic used above, list three stories or news items which have happened in the last week. You can use a newspaper to help.

2. Choose one of your news stories and write a TV news report on it. Remember, TV news reports are short and meant to be read by a reporter. Try writing a report which takes only 15 or 30 seconds to read.

3. Give your news report to a partner to read. If you can, videotape several news reports together and produce a TV news program.

Draw two other pictures to represent more idioms.

Grammar Power

1. Using vivid words: Just as an artist paints a picture with oils, a writer paints pictures with words. Words can be gloomy, gentle, funny, or fearsome.

Read the sentence pairs below.

> The puppy **ate** his food
> The puppy **devoured** his food.

What difference in meaning is created by changing the verb in the two sentences?

Use your imagination, a thesaurus, or a dictionary to write as many vivid words as possible for each of the words below.

> walk   eat   big   pretty

2. Using vivid expressions: Effective writers use colourful phrases and expressions to create vivid sentences. Notice the difference between the two sentences below.

> The sunlight reflected on the water.
> The shaft of sunlight danced on the water like sparkling diamonds.

Add vivid details to bring these colourless sentences to life.

> **a)** The school bus was noisy.
> **b)** We have many types of flowers in our garden.
> **c)** We paddled our canoe across the lake.
> **d)** We walked up the mountain.

A **thesaurus** is a special dictionary that lists synonyms for words.

Proofing Power

Proofread the paragraph below, then rewrite it correcting the errors.

I was looking in the food section of the paper last night and there was an article about what the Priminester of Canada eats. There was also a picture of an atractive chocalite cake and beside it was the recipe.

I read the ingredients an saw that cocao, eggs, and other things were needed. I started with a posative and plesent attitude, but got more and more frustrated when the eggs wouldn't seperate. I was getting desparate, so I threw everything in together.

When I finished, the cake looked like a creeture from outer space. I put a vegtable on its head for a hat. I'm not sure whether the Priminister would like it, but it tasted good!

31 Prefixes

trans- inter-
ex- sub-

transfer interchange
exclaim submarine

substitute
experiment
interchange
transportation
interfere
experience
interview
submarine
exclaim
international
extra
translate
subtract
expensive
expand
transfer
interrupt
transparent

Hamburgers

This is Nigel DeBarlo in a live <u>interview</u> with Frank Lee Greasie, the <u>international</u> king of hamburgers. Mr. Greasie, how did you get into hamburgers?
FRANK: Well, I was two years old when I had my first <u>experience</u> with a hamburger. I was heard to <u>exclaim</u> "Yum". Then all I had to do was <u>transfer</u> my love of eating burgers to cooking them.
NIGEL: Your chain sells hamburgers in 41 countries. Where will you <u>expand</u> next?
FRANK: Well, we're talking about opening a hamburger stand in Greenland. The trouble is with the <u>transportation</u> of supplies.
NIGEL: Why are Greasie Hamburgers such a success?
FRANK: Because we never <u>interfere</u> with our basic

burger. We don't <u>substitute</u> soy flour for beef. We encourage our customers to <u>experiment</u> with toppings at no <u>extra</u> cost. Our hamburgers are not <u>expensive</u> and our basic beef...
NIGEL: If I might <u>interrupt</u>, Mr. Greasie—isn't it a good idea to <u>interchange</u> some animal protein with healthier plant protein?
FRANK: Any change would <u>subtract</u> from the burger's fantastic popularity. And that would <u>translate</u> into lower profits.
NIGEL: Any big plans for the Greasie chain?
FRANK: I'd like to try <u>transparent</u> wrapping.
NIGEL: Best of luck, Mr. Greasie, and thanks.

Observing Patterns

1. Write the list words that match the following clues.
   a) has five syllables _____
   b) have four syllables _____ , _____ , _____
   c) has a double consonant _____

You need to look at the 6th and 7th letter of some words to find out on which page it belongs.

2. Write the list words that would be found on a dictionary page with each set of guide words.

  a) **transcontinental/transplant**
  b) **intercede/intravenous**
  c) **escape/extract**
  d) **subdivide/subway**

Discovering Patterns

substitute experiment interchange transportation interfere experience interview submarine exclaim international extra translate subtract expensive expand transfer interrupt transparent

1. Write the list words that begin with the prefix **sub-**. Underline the prefix in each word. When the prefix **sub-** begins a word, it usually means 'under' or 'below', as in **subway**. It may also mean 'further' or 'again', as in **subdivide**.

2. Write the list words that begin with the prefix **ex-**. Underline the prefix in each word. When the prefix **ex-** begins a word, it usually means 'out of', as in **express** (speak out), or 'from', as in **extend** (grow from).

3. Write the list words that begin with the prefix **inter-**. Underline the prefix in each word. When the prefix **inter-** begins a word, it usually means 'between', as in **interprovincial** (between provinces), or 'together', as in **interfold** (to fold together).

4. Write the list words that begin with the prefix **trans-**. Underline the prefix in each word. When the prefix **trans-** begins a word, it may mean 'over', as in **transmission** (sending over), 'through', as in **transit** (the act of passing through), or 'into a different condition', as in **transmute** (change from one form into another).

POWERBOOSTER

* The meaning and spelling of a word can be more easily understood when it is linked to the meaning of its prefix.

Exploring Patterns

1. Make a 'word-burger'! Combine the prefixes on the top bun, the word parts in the middle, and the endings on the bottom to write eight words.

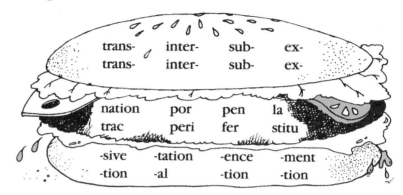

2. Substitute a list word for each underlined word or phrase in the following sentences. Write the sentences.

a) Please don't <u>start talking</u> when I begin to <u>question</u> the job applicant.

b) I don't have any <u>additional</u> money for that <u>costly</u> watch.

c) In our scientific <u>test</u>, we decided to <u>switch</u> helium for air in a large balloon. Then we watched the balloon <u>grow bigger</u> and float away.

3. Combine the prefix **inter-** with each adjective on the outer circle. Then use each word correctly in one of the sentences below.

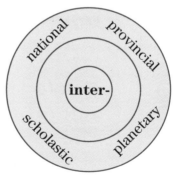

a) A track meet with competitors from Canada, Britain, and the United States in an _____ meet.

b) A space probe travelling from Earth to Mars is on an _____ space mission.

c) A meeting between the premiers of British Columbia, Manitoba, and Prince Edward Island is an _____ meeting.

d) A basketball game between Ryerson High School and Westport High School is an _____ game.

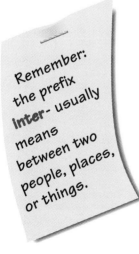

Remember: the prefix **inter-** usually means between two people, places, or things.

148

Use a dictionary to check how to divide words into syllables.

4. **Where's the stress?** The list words below contain three syllables. Copy the chart into your notebook. Then, complete the chart with list words, writing them in syllables with an accent on the stressed syllable.

| transparent | interview | substitute |
| interrupt | interfere | expensive |

stress on the first syllable	stress on the middle syllable	stress on the final syllable

5. **Enter a Contest!** Brainstorm with a partner to find a name and advertising slogan for hamburgers. Write down all the words you associate with hamburgers, then choose one for a name, and several others to make up your slogan. This name and slogan will be used in a chain of fast food stores around the world.

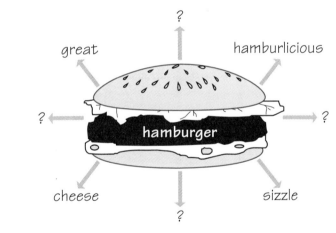

great   ?   hamburlicious

?   hamburger   ?

cheese   ?   sizzle

Challenges with Words

1. Write the Super Word that fits in each blank space below.

One of the most _____ stories in the history of food is the amazing _____ of the humble, beef patty into the magnificent _____ . The hamburger began in Hamburg, Germany, as raw, scraped beef. It is an excellent source of _____ as long as the meat used is not _____ . If it weren't for the _____ of adults, some children would eat hamburgers, with or without cheese, every day of their lives.

SUPER WORDS

interference
cheeseburger
transformation
protein
substandard
exceptional

2. a) There are many words in English that begin with the prefixes **inter-**, **sub-**, **trans-**.

Match these prefixes with the base words below.

divide form dependent face soil title
fusion plant lock urban planetary

b) Choose five of the expanded words you created above, and write sentences of your own. If possible, make the sentences connect in a story or a paragraph on a topic of your choice.

3. Your shiny hair, strong bones, and bright eyes depend on eating enough protein. Put a check beside each food you have eaten in the last two days. Add other foods you have eaten that you think contain protein. Now compare your 'protein profile' with a partner's.

beans	☐	lamb	☐
roast beef	☐	liver	☐
cheese	☐	lobster	☐
chicken	☐	milk	☐
eggs	☐	oatmeal	☐
fish	☐	pork chops	☐
ham	☐	shrimp	☐
hamburger	☐	yogurt	☐
ice cream	☐		

4. The original hamburger recipe called for raw meat, mixed with onion juice. Sound delicious? Write your own recipe for a totally outrageous and delicious hamburger. Remember to write it in two parts:
- the listing of ingredients;
- the method of mixing and cooking.

5. Many mouth-watering food sensations compete with hamburgers for our fast-food dollar. Match the descriptions below with the words at the left.
   a) french fries, topped with cheese and gravy
   b) Middle East treat, made entirely of vegetable protein
   c) an Italian delight, often filled with meat and/or cheese

NEW WORDS

falafel
calzone
poutine

32 Prefixes
dis- un-
disagree **un**known

dishonest
lose
sounds
unexciting
disappoint
unpopular
weird
travelled
taught
disagree
listen
unpaid
discourage
musician
whether
unknown
whose
boards

Violins

Violinists can be popular or unpopular, depending on whether they're making weird, screechy sounds, or beautiful music. But few would disagree that a violin is a versatile instrument. It can be played by an unpaid and unknown street musician, or a world-famous virtuoso.

This is Amy Wong at the Concert Hall. Tonight, I'm going to listen to a violin which has travelled from Italy. That might sound unexciting, but this violin was made in 1716 by the Italian, Guarnieri, whose violins are still among the best in the world. It might be the special boards he used that made his violins sound so great, but no one really knows his secret.

I hate to disappoint any of you who were planning to rush out and buy a Guarnieri. The price of a half-million dollars might discourage you. However, if you did own such a valuable violin, I'm sure you'd hate to lose it. That's what almost happened to Alexander Schneider, a violinist who left his $200 000 Guarnieri in a New York taxi. He was lucky that the next passengers were not dishonest. They returned the instrument to Schneider. I'm sure that experience taught him to be more careful with his priceless violin.

It's time to take my seat, front row centre. This is Amy Wong, signing off for Kids' Report.

Observing Patterns

1. Write the list words that fit the following clues.
    a) the sound /ē/ as in **me** is spelled **ei** _____
    b) the sound /h/ is spelled **wh** _____
    c) contains a **silent h** _____ , _____
    d) contains a **silent t** _____
    e) the sound /sh/ is spelled **ci** _____

2. Write the list words that rhyme with the following:
  a) swords
  b) choose
  c) pounds
  d) caught

3. Write the list words, in alphabetical order, that would be found on a dictionary page with the following sets of guide words.

disable / discover

d i s _ _ _ _ _
d i s _ _ _ _ _ _ _
d i s _ _ _ _ _ _

uneasy / unprepared

u n _ _ _ _ _ _ _
u n _ _ _ _ _
u n _ _ _ _
u n _ _ _ _ _ _

4. Write the list words that match these shapes.

| | | | | | | | | | | | | | | | | | | | | | | | | | | | | | | | | | | | |

Discovering Patterns

dishonest lose sounds unexciting disappoint unpopular weird travelled taught disagree listen unpaid discourage musician whether unknown whose boards

1. Write the list words that begin with the prefix **dis-**. Underline the prefix in each word. When the prefix **dis-** is added to a base word, it usually means 'not' as in **disobey**.

2. Write the list words that begin with the prefix **un-**. Underline the prefix in each word. When the prefix **un-** is added to a base word, it usually means 'not' as in **unkind**.

POWERBOOSTER

• The prefixes **dis-** and **un-**, when added to a base word, usually mean 'not'.

Exploring Patterns

1. Write the list words that are similar in meaning to the words and phrases below.

a) untrustworthy	**b**) still owing
c) boring	**d**) fail to satisfy
e) disliked	**f**) quarrel with
g) take away hope or confidence	**h**) not familiar; strange

2. A **musician** is someone who is trained in music. Name the term used to describe someone who is trained in each of the following:

    a) magic   _ _ _ _ _ i a n
    b) electricity   _ _ _ _ _ _ _ i a n
    c) technical details   _ _ _ _ _ _ i a n
    d) planning balanced diets for others   _ _ _ _ _ i a n

3. Complete each sentence by adding **dis-** or **un-** to the underlined word. Write the sentences.

    a) I was <u>impressed</u> with some of the paintings but quite _____ by other works.
    b) The baseball player had the <u>advantage</u> of being a good fielder but the _____ of being a weak hitter.
    c) The rabbit <u>appeared</u> in our yard, but quickly _____ when the dog barked.
    d) In the middle of summer the beaches are often <u>polluted</u>, but right now they are _____ .

4. The list word **whose** is a possessive form of **who**, as in: "That is the musician whose violin is so valuable," or "Whose instrument is this?"

Be careful not to confuse **whose** with the contraction **who's** as in "Who's coming with me?" or, "There is the girl who's performing in the concert."

Complete each sentence with **whose** or **who's**.

    a) _____ bicycle is lying on the walk?
    b) Do you know _____ coming to the practice?
    c) I'm not certain _____ boots these are.
    d) _____ interested in a game of checkers?

POLLUTED WATER
NO SWIMMING

OPEN

For a review of possessives go back to Unit 14.

5. Complete the following analogies by using list words.

  a) soccer player is to **athlete** as **violinist** is to _____

  b) catch is to **caught** as **teach** is to _____

  c) look is to **see** as _____ is to **hear**

  d) unusual is to **uncommon** as un**familiar** is to _____

6. Imagine that, like Schneider, you have left something valuable in a taxi, bus, or train. Make a **LOST** poster to advertise your loss. Be sure to describe in detail what you've lost. Include a reward, if you think it might help get your lost object back.

Challenges with Words

1. Unscramble the 'letter-notes' below to write words which are related in meaning to each Super Word. Use the clues below to help you.

  a) a violin is one

  b) an orchestra needs many

  c) a synonym for **unbelievable**

  d) an antonym for **unfortunately**

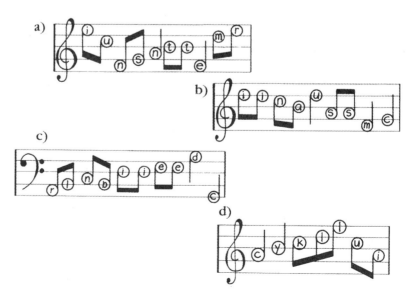

violin
orchestra
unbelievable
unfortunately
disqualified
disobedience

154

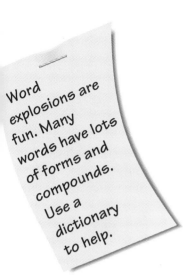

Word explosions are fun. Many words have lots of forms and compounds. Use a dictionary to help.

2. The Super Word **disobedience** is part of a family of words related to **obey**. Explode the word **obey**, and fill in as many of the other **obey** words as you can.

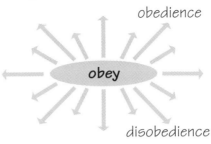

obedience

obey

disobedience

3. Make similar word explosions for **fortune** and **belief**.

◄ WORDS IN HISTORY ►

> The Super Word **violin** is named after the **viol**, a stringed instrument which was also played with a bow.

Find the word origins of two other musical instruments.

4. Match these modern instruments to their word origins.

Instrument	Origin
harp	kithara (Greek)
flute	trompette (Old French)
trumpet	hearpe (Anglo-Saxon)
guitar	clarus (Latin)
clarinet	flatus (Latin)

5. Write a newspaper report about an **unbelievable** event or situation. Try to use some of the Super Words in your article.

Example:

Animal Orchestra Plays it Up

Pet City, Canada. Animals from across Canada spent the weekend competing in the first, annual <u>Animal Music Festival</u>. Audiences and judges alike enjoyed orchestra concertos as well as full symphonies . . .

Prefixes

re- com- con- pre- pro-

review **com**pare **con**tent
prepare **pro**gress

sentence
conference
progress
professor
worst
review
happens
fantasy
compare
wondered
English
content
predict
poem
rhyme
rewrite
prepare
composition

Words into Poetry

This is Alexander Douglas with Ian Lake, the famous poet and <u>professor</u> of <u>English</u>. Professor Lake, I <u>wondered</u> if you could tell us what <u>happens</u> when you begin to write a <u>poem</u>?

PROFESSOR LAKE: Well, I usually <u>prepare</u> by thinking about the <u>content</u> of the poem for quite a while. So I <u>progress</u> quite rapidly when I actually begin to write.

ALEXANDER: How long does the actual writing or <u>composition</u> of a poem take?

PROFESSOR LAKE: I can never <u>predict</u> how long it will take. The first draft is usually quite fast.

ALEXANDER: Do you often <u>rewrite</u> your poetry?

PROFESSOR LAKE: Yes, I like to put the first draft away, and <u>review</u> it weeks later.

ALEXANDER: Do you ever <u>conference</u> with other writers?

PROFESSOR LAKE: I often conference with myself—I like to <u>compare</u> the finished poem with my rough drafts, read it out loud, and listen to the rhythms—that sort of thing.

ALEXANDER: Professor Lake, do you think it's important for poems to <u>rhyme</u>?

PROFESSOR LAKE: Some of the <u>worst</u> poetry rhymes, some of the best does not.

Observing Patterns

1. Write the list words that fit the following clues.
    a) contain double consonants _____ , _____ , _____
    b) the sound /r/ is spelled **wr** _____
    c) the sound /r/ is spelled **rh** _____

2. Write the list words that are related to the following words.

a) poetry   _____

b) worse   _____

c) fantastic   _____

d) rhythm   _____

e) England   _____

Discovering Patterns

sentence conference progress professor worst review happens fantasy compare wondered English content predict poem rhyme rewrite prepare composition

1. Write the list words that begin with the prefix **pre-**. Underline the prefix in each word. When the prefix **pre-** begins a word, it usually means 'before', as in **prepay** (pay before), and **prejudge** (judge before).

2. Write the list words that begin with the prefix **re-**. Underline the prefix in each word. When the prefix **re-** begins a word, it usually means 'back', or 'again', as in **recall** (call back), and **rebuild** (build again).

3. Write the list words that begin with the prefix **pro-**. Underline the prefix in each word. When the prefix **pro-** begins a word, it usually means 'forward', as in **propel** (drive forward), and **propose** (put forward).

4. Write the list words that begin with the prefixes **con-** or **com-**. Underline the prefix in each word. When the prefixes **con-** or **com-** begin a word, they usually mean 'together', as in **concoct** (put together), and **compile** (bring together).

The prefix pre- usually means 'before'.

POWERBOOSTER

- The meaning of a word can often be found by linking the meaning of the base word with the meaning of its prefix.

Exploring Patterns

1. Complete this limerick with list words.

There once was a p_____ named Fred,
Who tried to write p_____s in his head.
He w_____ each time
About rhythm and r_____ ,
And got the w_____ headache instead!

2. How many words can you make by adding suffixes to each base word in the circle? At least two suffixes can be added to each base.

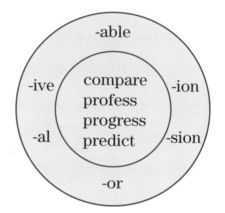

3. Complete each sentence with list words. Some of the beginning letters have been included for you.

   a) Would you like to r_____ your last test with me? It may help you to _____ for tomorrow's quiz.
   b) I like to c_____ the first draft of my _____ with the final version. I usually _____ parts I don't like, or change some of the _____ . It's interesting to see how I p_____ from the rough draft to the finished work.

4. The words **progress** and **content** are pronounced in two ways depending upon how they are used in a sentence. The stress is placed on either the first or second syllable. For each sentence below, rewrite the underlined word and circle the stressed syllable. What part of speech is **progress** and **content** in each of these sentences.

   a) Your report card shows excellent <u>progress</u>.
   b) I hope we can <u>progress</u> to the next level of swimming.
   c) Are you <u>content</u> with the shoes you bought?
   d) I enjoyed the <u>content</u> of your report very much.

5. Work in a group and interview someone in your group who likes to be creative—write, play music, dance, draw, or build things. What would you like to find out about the way they work? Before the interview write an outline of the questions you'd like to ask. You might want to tape-record your interview.

condense
rhythm
proficient
preface
readjust
compassionate

Challenges with Words

1. Complete each set with a Super Word.
   a) sympathetic, charitable, _____
   b) abbreviate, compact, _____
   c) introduction, foreword, _____
   d) skilful, able, _____
   e) realign, reorder, _____
   f) metre, cadence, _____

2. A **preface** is an introduction to a book. Here are some other parts of a book. Arrange them in the order you think they would appear.
   a) foreword   **b)** appendix
   c) index   **d)** dedication
   e) table of contents **f)** bibliography

3. Four of the Super Words begin with the prefix **con-**, **pre-**, **re-**, or **com-**. They have base words which can be found in the dictionary.
   a) Write the meaning of each base word.
   b) Write the meaning of each prefix.

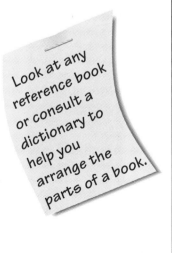

Look at any reference book or consult a dictionary to help you arrange the parts of a book.

Condense some words and write word clues of your own.

4. Condense the following words to match the word clues. Use only letters found in the original word, but you may put them in any order. You'll need to be a **proficient** wordsmith to do these!

Example: ***breakfast**—a three-letter word meaning a hot drink you might have for **breakfast** (tea)*

a) compose—a four-letter word that names something a writer might **compose**

b) disobeys—a three-letter word that tells what a child might do after he or she **disobeys**

c) provides—a four-letter word that names something a bakery **provides**

d) detour—a five-letter word that tells what you need to make a **detour**

5. Prefix Madness: Use the letters in the box to make words which match the definitions below. You may use each letter as many times as you like.

b	r	g	p	e	c	t
o	a	m	d	s	n	i

distant, far away   **re** _____   give approval   **con** _____
give orders   **com** _____   reduce in rank   **de** _____

6. Write other words that you know that begin with these prefixes.

con- com- de- pre- pro- re-

7. Rank the Super Words by difficulty of spelling from easiest to hardest. Compare your ranking with a partner's. Write a 'list of tricks' for spelling these challenging words. For example: **Rhythm:**

Example: ***Rhythm**—I always spell this word out loud in my head. I remember there's a **rhythm** to the sound of the letters (**rhy/thm**).*

8. New sports are being invented all the time. Other sports have been around for many years but have recently become popular. Complete each sentence below with the correct new word.

a) In a _____ the athletes compete in swimming, bicycling, and running.

b) When you go _____ you are flown to the top of a mountain in a helicopter.

c) Hot air _____ was developed in the late 1700s.

Prefixes, Suffixes, Capital Letters

unhappiness Edmonton

unemployment
tennis
calm
neighbour
French
Newfoundland
series
knock
zero
ninety
garage
Tuesday
April
Edmonton
knees
disgraceful
unhappiness
independent

Tennis Tournament

This is Beverley Windsor on the <u>tennis</u> court. I'm training hard these days and also learning to speak <u>French</u>. Next year, I'm competing in a junior tennis tournament in France.

I've played tennis since I was eight or nine years old. I started in <u>Edmonton</u> by hitting tennis balls against the <u>garage</u> wall next door. It used to drive our <u>neighbour</u> crazy. My <u>knees</u> would <u>knock</u> when he came over to complain, but I couldn't stop. It was <u>disgraceful</u>, but I was hooked on the game. Any worry or <u>unhappiness</u> in my life and I'd be out there, hitting balls. A few minutes of tennis, and I'd be <u>calm</u> again.

I'd practise from <u>April</u> until November, even when the temperature fell below <u>zero</u>. It made me feel <u>independent</u>. At the age of ten, I began a <u>series</u> of tennis lessons. Each <u>Tuesday</u>, I was coached by a tennis pro who, at the time, was experiencing a period of <u>unemployment</u>. My game began to improve. I could now hit the ball against the neighbour's wall at <u>ninety</u> kilometres per hour. Shortly afterward, we moved to St. John's, <u>Newfoundland</u>. In St. John's, I joined a tennis club and now I compete in local tournaments. I hope all this work pays off in France!

Observing Patterns

1. Write the list words that fit the following clues.
   a) the sound /n/ is spelled **kn** _____ , _____
   b) are numbers _____ , _____
   c) the letter **l** is silent _____
   d) the sound /ā/ is spelled **eigh** _____

2. Complete the following sets with list words.
   a) January, February, March, _____
   b) porch, attic, basement, _____
   c) New Brunswick, Nova Scotia, Prince Edward Island, _____
   d) Calgary, Lethbridge, Red Deer, _____

3. Complete each sentence with a list word.
   a) The numbers 2, 4, 6, 8, 10 represent a _____ .
   b) The behaviour of the rowdy spectators was _____ .
   c) I'm not able to come on Monday, but I'm free on _____ .
   d) The official languages of Canada are English and _____ .

Discovering Patterns

unemployment tennis calm
neighbour French Newfoundland
series knock zero ninety garage
Tuesday April Edmonton knees
disgraceful unhappiness independent

1. Write the following list words.

independent	unemployment
disgraceful	unhappiness

Beside each word write the base word. Notice that in each case a suffix or ending has been added to the base word.

The three prefixes **dis-**, **un-**, and **in-**, all can mean 'not' when added to a base word. What effect does each prefix have on the meaning of the base words you have written?

2. Write in the following order the list words that are capitalized.
   a) days of the week   **b)** months of the year
   c) places   **d)** languages

POWERBOOSTER

- The meaning and spelling of long words can often be made easier by breaking each word into a prefix, base word, and suffix.
- Names of people, places, months, and days begin with capital letters.

Exploring Patterns

1. Unscramble the list word on each tennis ball.

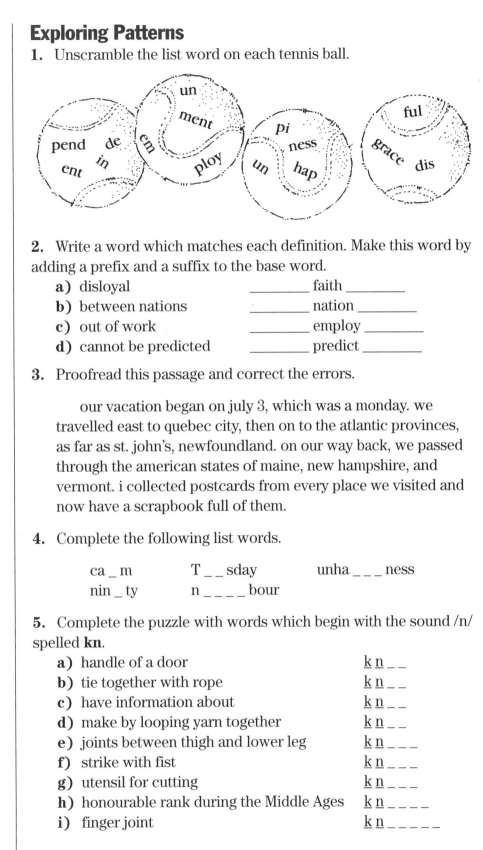

2. Write a word which matches each definition. Make this word by adding a prefix and a suffix to the base word.

    a) disloyal   _____ faith _____

    b) between nations   _____ nation _____

    c) out of work   _____ employ _____

    d) cannot be predicted   _____ predict _____

3. Proofread this passage and correct the errors.

       our vacation began on july 3, which was a monday. we travelled east to quebec city, then on to the atlantic provinces, as far as st. john's, newfoundland. on our way back, we passed through the american states of maine, new hampshire, and vermont. i collected postcards from every place we visited and now have a scrapbook full of them.

4. Complete the following list words.

       ca _ m   T _ _ sday   unha _ _ _ ness

       nin _ ty   n _ _ _ _ bour

5. Complete the puzzle with words which begin with the sound /n/ spelled **kn**.

    a) handle of a door   k n _ _

    b) tie together with rope   k n _ _

    c) have information about   k n _ _

    d) make by looping yarn together   k n _ _

    e) joints between thigh and lower leg   k n _ _ _

    f) strike with fist   k n _ _ _

    g) utensil for cutting   k n _ _ _

    h) honourable rank during the Middle Ages k n _ _ _ _

    i) finger joint   k n _ _ _ _ _

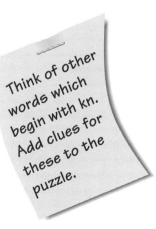

Think of other words which begin with kn. Add clues for these to the puzzle.

Fredericton
competitive
unnatural
recreation
Inuvik
tournament

6. Do you remember learning to swim? ride a bicycle? skate? Often first experiences are frustrating or funny.

Write about your recollections of learning a sport, or becoming involved in an activity, such as volunteer work. You may want to write an outline such as the one below before you begin.

• first impressions of the sport or activity
• how you felt when you started
• one or two incidents that stand out in your mind
• whether you decided to give up the sport or activity, or stick with it
• how you feel about it now

Challenges with Words

1. Use the Super Words to complete this paragraph.

Whether it's Arctic Winter Games in _____ , or a volleyball _____ in _____ , New Brunswick, sports meets are big news in Canada these days. Doctors tell us that people of all ages and types need _____ for the body as well as the mind. It's _____ for the human body not to play and exercise. Some of Canada's most famous athletes like Rick Hansen and Terry Fox have proved that physical activity is for everyone, whether you play a _____ sport or just want to have fun.

2. Add the correct prefix, suffix, or both to complete each Super Word below.

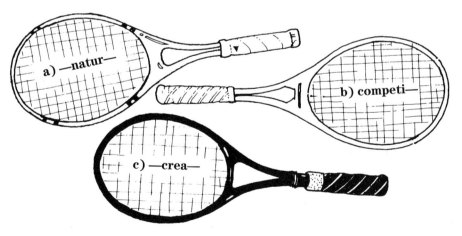

a) —natur—

b) competi—

c) —crea—

3. Many cities and towns, such as **Fredericton**, are named after people. Use a dictionary or encyclopedia to write the names of five Canadian towns or cities and the people who inspired their names.

The Super Word **tournament** originally meant 'tourney', a medieval jousting match between knights on horseback. It comes from the old French word **torneiement**.

4. A **tournament** is a series of contests which tests the skills of the participants. Write the sport which matches the following events.

    a) bonspiel   **b)** Triple Crown

    c) Grey Cup   **d)** Wimbledon

    e) Stanley Cup

5. a) Work with a partner. Brainstorm for ideas that come to mind when you think of the word **recreation**.

b) Cluster the words in two or more categories. Choose one category and write a story or report, using as many of the words you wrote as possible.

disobedience   summer

recreation

165

STUDY STEPS

LOOK
SAY
COVER
WRITE
CHECK

Here is a list of challenging words from Units 31–34.

interrupt	disappoint	unexciting	independent
Tuesday	calm	musician	taught
listen	lose	whose	whether
weird	composition	worst	poem
rhyme	knock	ninety	neighbour

1. Use the Study Steps for each word. Your teacher will then dictate the words.

2. Complete the following story with words from the Study List. Some beginning letters have been supplied for you. Use each word only once.

Last night I was working on a c_____ that must be finished by _____ . The _____ part was deciding on a topic. My ideas seemed either _____ (My Favourite School Subject) or too w_____ (Why My Goldfish are Depressed). Then I remembered what we had been _____ about writing, that we should l_____ to our own thoughts. I told my brother and sister not to _____ me, and I tried to _____ down and l_____ myself in the albums of my favourite m_____ . When I heard a _____ on my door about _____ minutes later, I had already written the first draft of a p_____ about an elderly _____ of ours w_____ fascinating stories about 'the old days' are just incredible. I'm not sure w_____ the poem will _____ or not, but I know I won't d_____ myself by the time I'm finished.

3. Write the review words that rhyme with the following.

a) clock _____ **b)** choose _____ , _____
c) beard _____ **d)** time _____
e) burst _____

4. Write the review words that match these shapes.

| |ıı|ıı   ıı|ı| ı|ı|ıı   ııı|||ıı   ı|ı|||ıı

5. Complete each review word.
    a) T _ _ sday   **b)** music _ _ n
    c) nin _ ty   **d)** inte _ _ upt
    e) p _ _ m   **f)** disa _ _ oint

6. Write words that are homophones for **not**, **no**, **new**, and **night**.

7. Write the antonyms of the following words. Each word should begin with the prefix **dis-** or **un-**.
    a) popular
    b) agree
    c) exciting
    d) known
    e) honest

8. Write the words with prefixes from the box which match the following definitions.
    a) a ship that operates under the surface of the ocean _____
    b) to look at something again _____
    c) to forecast events before they happen _____
    d) something you can see through _____
    e) an event taking place between nations _____
    f) to call or shout _____
    g) to move forward; grow _____
    h) a meeting of people with a similar interest _____

predict
review
transparent
international
submarine
conference
progress
exclaim

9. a) Combine the prefixes, word parts, and suffixes to make four English words. You may use any word part more than once.

    b) Use each word you have formed in a sentence.

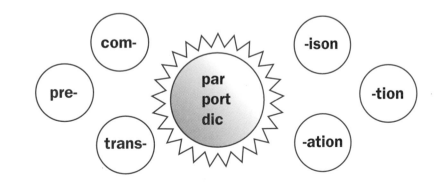

167

Dictionary Skills

1. Homographs: Homographs are words which are spelled the same but have different meanings, pronunciations, or origins. Each word has a separate entry in the dictionary with a number above it.

a) Read the entries for the word **content**. Depending upon where the stress is placed, this word has two very different meanings.

con•tent[1] (kon´tent) **1** the facts or ideas stated; what is written in a book or said in a speech. **2** the proportion of a certain substance contained in something else: the sugar content of a dessert.

con•tent[2] (kən tent´) satisfied; not desiring anything more or anything different than what one has.

b) Which entry (1 or 2) for the word **content**, matches each sentence below? Write the correct entry number on the blank beside each sentence.

_____ Is there something in the <u>content</u> of the story that you don't understand?

_____ We'll have to be <u>content</u> with whatever movies are available.

_____ Cream has a higher fat <u>content</u> than milk.

2. Etymology: Some dictionary entries contain information about the etymology or origin of the word.

The names of the days of the week and the months of the year have interesting etymologies. For example, Thursday comes from the Old English word thursdæg, meaning 'day of thunder' or 'day of Thor' (the Germanic god of thunder).

a) Find information in the Mini-Dictionary about the etymology of the words **Tuesday** and **April**.

b) Match the words in Column A with the original meaning in Column B. The Mini-Dictionary will help you.

Column A	Column B
maintain	seasickness
noise	empty
zero	hold by the hand

Saturday Night Special

1. TV news magazines, shows, or journals combine both the length of a newspaper story and the action of a TV newscast.

a) List five types of reports or news items you might include in this week's show. They might be a story about an interesting personality, a current news issue, a major sports event, or anything else you think people would be interested in seeing.

b) Choose one of your reports and outline how you would develop the report for the show. You could use interviews in the studio or on location, have a panel of experts discussing the topic, include live-action video footage, and so on.

Write your outline in the form of a memo to your producer. You might use this form.

Watch a TV news show for ideas on how to present your news items.

MEMO

Date: (Today's date)
To: (Name of your producer)
From: (Your name)
Subject: SATURDAY NIGHT SPECIAL

1. Announcer introduces topic over video footage of. . .
2.
3.

(and so on)

Grammar Power

1. Audience and voice: It is important for writers to think about the people who will be reading or hearing their message. We call this group (or person) the **audience**.

Read the two letters below. They are both written by Andrea, who is in trouble because she forgot to pick up her younger sister.

Dear Ms. Bruner,

I missed gym class yesterday due to a family commitment. I was supposed to pick up my little sister, Ciara, at her ballet class at noon. Unfortunately, I forgot and realized just before your class that Ciara would be waiting for me.

I would be glad to make up the class time after school today if it is all right with you.

Yours sincerely,

Andrea

Dear Ciara,

I know you're really upset with me and I don't blame you. How could I have forgotten you? Sometimes I think I have noodles where my brain should be. Anyway I owe you one.

Sorry again!

Andrea

P.S. You may borrow any one of my CDs for a week!

a) Who is the audience for each letter?

b) How does the language differ between the two letters?

2. One letter is very informal or casual and the other is more formal. We refer to these levels of language as **voice**.

Write two letters as outlined below. Before you begin, think about who your **audience** is for each letter and the **voice** you wish to use.

a) Write a friendly letter to a close friend who has moved away. You might wish to thank your friend for a special gift, describe what is happening at school, give news about your family, and so forth.

b) Write a formal request for information for a school project. This letter could be sent to a company, a government agency, or an individual.

Proofing Power

Read the passage below, then rewrite it correcting the errors.

On Teusday my family rented a rather wierd movie about a musicain who had to choose wether to stick with his music or change careers. He had taight himself to play the guitar, but was the werst player I've ever heard!

He wanted to be independant, so he moved into his own apartment. His nieghbour didn't like his playing either. One night he heard a nock at the door. The police said they had been called about a disturbance in his apartement. The musician tried to remain calme but felt himself starting to loose control. How could anyone not enjoy his music?

All in all, it was a very unexciteing movie. Don't waste your money!

Basic Word List

absorb
action
actor
addition
addresses
admiration
admit
adult
advantage
advertisement
affection
alert
alphabets
American
amusement
ancient
annoyed
April
argument
arranged
attitude
attractive
average
avoid
awareness
awful

balance
banquet
barefoot
baseball
beaches
beard
beautiful
because
beginning

believe
below
between
billion
birth
blurred
boards
bomb
bored
bottles
bowl
branches
bright
brilliant
broadcast
burden
burning
bury

calm
camera
Canadian
canals
capable
capital
carefree
careful
cartoon
centuries
cereal
certainly
champions
changed
changes
characters
chart

check
chocolate
choice
choose
chuckled
chute
cities
clipboard
clubhouse
coach
coarse
coast
cocoa
codes
coins
collected
collision
combination
comfortable
comic
compare
compete
competition
complete
composition
concentration
conclude
conclusion
condition
conference
confusion
connection
conserve
consumer
containers
content

contest
contribution
conversation
convert
co-operate
copied
course
craft
crater
created
creature
credit
creep
crime
crouch
crystal
culture
currency
cushion

darken
dazzle
delicate
delicious
denied
dentist
department
depth
desperate
destroy
detective
dialling
diamond
different
digital

dimension
director
dirty
disagree
disappoint
discourage
disgrace
disgraceful
dishonest
display
distance
divided
doesn't
dollar
domestic
double
doubt
dragged
dramatic
drowned
dwarf

earthquake
edible
edit
Edmonton
education
effective
elaborate
emerald
emission
employed
endless
English
enjoyable
erosion

170

erupt
escape
excellent
except
exchange
exclaim
exhibition
expand
expensive
experience
experiment
expert
explain
explore
explosion
extra
extreme

factory
failure
fantasy
farther
fashion
feathers
fertile
figure
film
fitted
flute
fooled
football
forceful
forgetting
formula
fortunate
forward
fossil

foul
fourth
fragments
freight
French
friendly
frighten
funds
furious

garage
garment
gently
giant
glasses
glitter
goalie's
grabbed
grand
groove
growth

half
happens
hardly
harmless
hasn't
he'd
heard
heavy
hidden
highland
history
hopeless
humorous
hurry

ignorant
ignore
illustrated
image
imagine
important
impossible
impressive
independent
industry
infield
ingredients
injury
instant
instruction
interchange
interfere
international
interrupt
interview
introduction
invasion
invention
irrigate
item

join
juicy

knees
knew
knock

larva
lava
league
lessons

letters
libraries
lift
listen
lock
lonely
lose
loudspeaker
lovely
luckily

maintain
manager
manufacture
marble
marriage
media
message
method
Mexican
migrate
mineral
missed
mist
moist
molten
moment
multiply
musician
mustache
mysterious

nation
necessary
nectar
neighbour
nervous

Newfoundland
nickel
ninety
nuisance

ocean
office
official
opening
opponents'
orbit
original
outlook
ownership

panic
patient
patio
patterns
penalty
people
permitting
personal
photo
pianos
pictures
piece
pirate
pitied
plantation
player's
players'
pleasant
pleasure
pocket
poem
poison

polish
positive
powerful
predict
preferred
prepare
presently
president
principal
principle
private
prize
proceed
process
produced
profession
professor
progress
propeller
protective
provide
published
pupa
pupae
purchase
putty
puzzle

quote

really
recent
referee's
release
relief
responsible
review

rewrite
rhyme

sandal
satisfaction
satisfying
scale
scientists
scoreboard
scurry
season
sensitive
sentence
separate
sergeant
serial
series
serious
servant
shall
shelves
shoot
shortstop
shouldn't
shouted
shutter
signature
signs
skill
slammed
sleigh
slight
smash
soccer
social
softness
someday

sounds
source
sparkling
speech
spirit
stage
standard
starvation
stolen
storage
stories
straight
strait
stray
strip
stroke
student's
students'
studying
submarine
substitute
subtract
success
sugarless
suggest
suitable
sunken
surprise
swirls
switch
syrup
systems

target
taught
teamwork
telephone

tennis
tension
terrific
theatre
themselves
they've
thousands
threw
title
toast
torture
total
towering
tragic
transfer
transform
translate
transparent
transportation
travelled
trick
tripped
Tuesday
tunnel
type

ugliness
understand
unemployment
unexciting
unhappiness
unknown
unless
unload
unpaid
unpopular
urgent

valuable
vary
vegetable
very
visible
vital

wade
washable
wealthy
weigh
weighed
weird
whether
whole
whose
wicked
widely
winning
wondered
wood
worried
worst
worthless
would
wouldn't
wrinkles

you're
yourself

zero

a	hat, cap	**i**	it, pin	**p**	paper, cup	**z**	zero, breeze
ā	age, face	**ī**	ice, five	**r**	run, try	**zh**	measure, seizure
ä	barn, far			**s**	say, yes		
				sh	she, rush	**ə**	represents:
b	bad, rob	**j**	jam, enjoy	**t**	tell, it		a in about
ch	child, much	**k**	kind, seek	**th**	thin, both		e in taken
d	did, red	**l**	land, coal	**ŦH**	then, smooth		i in pencil
		m	me, am				o in lemon
		n	no, in				u in circus
e	let, best	**ng**	long, bring	**u**	cup, butter		
ē	equal, be			**u̇**	full, put		
er	care, bear			**ü**	rule, move		
ėr	term, learn	**o**	hot, rock	**yü**	use, music		
		ō	open, go				
f	fat, if	**ô**	order, door	**v**	very, save		
g	go, bag	**oi**	oil, voice	**w**	will, woman		
h	he, how	**ou**	house, out	**y**	young, yet		

A ▼▼▼

ab·sorb [ab zôrb′ *or* ab sôrb′]   **1** take in or suck up liquids. **2** take up all the attention of; interest very much. *v.*

ac·tion [ak′shən]   **1** the process of doing something; acting. **2** the way in which something moves or works. *n.*

ac·tor [ak′tər]   **1** a person who acts on the stage, in motion pictures, or on television or radio. **2** a person who does something or takes part in something. *n.*

ad·di·tion [ə dish′ən]   **1** the adding of one number or quantity to another: *2 + 2 = 4 is a simple addition.* **2** the adding of one thing to another. *n.*
in addition or **in addition to,** besides: *In addition to the money for their work, the girls received free lunches.*

ad·dress [ə dres′ *or* ad′res]   **1** the place at which a person, business, etc. may be found or reached. **2** write on an envelope or package the information that shows where it is to be sent. **1** *n.,* **2** *v.*

ad·mi·ra·tion [ad′mə rā′shən]   **1** a feeling of wonder, pleasure, and approval. **2** a person or thing that is admired. *n.*

ad·mit [ad mit′]   **1** say something is real or true. **2** allow to enter. *v.,* **ad·mit·ted, ad·mit·ting.**

a·dult [ə dult′ *or* ad′ult]   **1** fully developed and mature; full-grown; grown-up. **2** a grown-up person. **3** a full-grown animal or plant. **1** *adj.,* **2, 3** *n.*

ad·van·tage [ad van′tij]   something that is favourable; benefit or profit.

ad·ver·tise·ment [ad′vər tīz′mənt *or* ad vėr′tis mənt]   a public announcement or printed notice, especially one trying to persuade people to buy a product or service: *The store has an advertisement in the newspaper. n.*

af·fec·tion [ə fek′shən]   a friendly feeling; fondness; love. *n.*

a·lert [ə lėrt′]   **1** watchful; wide-awake. **2** warn of an attack. **1** *adj.,* **2** *v.* —**a·lert′ness,** *n.*

al·pha·bet [al′fə bet′]   the set of letters used in writing a language. *n.*

A·mer·i·can [ə mer′ə kən]   **1** a person born in or living in the United States. **2** of or having to do with the United States or its people: *an American citizen, American history.* **3** of, having to do with, or found in the western hemisphere: *the Amazon and other American rivers.* **1** *n.,* **2, 3** *adj.*

a·muse·ment [ə myüz′mənt]   **1** enjoyment; pleasure; being amused. **2** anything that amuses; entertainment; sport. *n.*

an·cient [ān′shənt]   **1** belonging to times long past. **2** very old: *An ancient house stood on the corner.* **3 the ancients**, people who lived long ago, especially the Greeks and Romans. *adj.*

an·noy [ə noi′]   tease; bother; disturb; make angry. *v.*

A·pril [ā′prəl]   the fourth month of the year. April has thirty days. *n.*
☛ *Etymology.* **April** came into English in the Middle Ages from the Latin name for this month.

ar·gu·ment [är′gyə mənt]   **1** a discussion by persons who give reasons for and against different points of view; a debate. **2** an emotional disagreement; a dispute: *He had an argument with his brother about who won the card game. n.*

ar·range [ə rānj′]   **1** put in the proper order. **2** plan; form plans. *v.,* **ar·ranged, ar·rang·ing.**

artificial intelligence [är′tə fish′əl in tel′ə jəns]   the ability of some computers to recognize and solve problems in ways that simulate human learning and reasoning.

173

ASAP   as soon as possible.

ATM   *Computer technology.* automated teller machine.

at·ti·tude   [at′ə tyüd′ *or* at′ə tüd′]   **1** one's way of thinking, acting, or feeling. **2** a position of the body suggesting an action, purpose, emotion, etc., *n.*

at·trac·tive   [ə trak′tiv]   pleasing; winning attention and liking. *adj.*

av·er·age   [av′ə rij]   **1** in arithmetic, the quantity found by dividing the sum of several quantities by the number of those quantities. **2** find the average of. **3** obtained by averaging. 1 *n.*, 2 *v.*, **av·er·aged, av·er·ag·ing;** 3 *adj.*

a·void   [ə void′]   keep away from; keep out of the way of. *v.* —**a·void′a·ble,** *adj.*

a·ware   [ə wer′]   knowing; realizing; conscious. *adj.* —**a·ware′ness,** *n.*

aw·ful   [of′əl]   **1** dreadful; causing fear. **2** impressive; deserving great respect. **3** *Informal.* very bad, great, ugly, etc. *adj.*

B ▼▼▼

bal·ance   [bal′əns]   **1** a steady condition or position; steadiness. **2** keep or put in a steady condition or position. **3** the part that is left over; the remainder. 1, 3 *n.*, 2 *v.* **bal·anced, bal·anc·ing.**

bal·loon·ing   [bə lü′ning]   the sport of riding in the basket of a hot-air balloon. *v.*

bank card   [bangk′ kärd′]   a small plastic card for electronic banking. It gives access to one or more of the user's bank accounts through a personal identification number (PIN) and can be used in automated teller machines (ATM), debit machines in stores, etc. *n.*

ban·quet   [bang′kwit]   a formal dinner or a feast, often with speeches. *n.*

bare·foot   [ber′fut′]   without shoes and stockings on. *adj.* or *adv.*

ba·rom·e·ter   [bə rom′ə tər]   **1** an instrument for measuring the pressure of the air and determining height above sea level: *A barometer shows probable changes in the weather.* **2** something that indicates changes: *Newspapers are often called barometers of public opinion.* *n.*

base·ball   [bas′bol′]   a game played with bat and ball by two teams of nine players each, on a field with four bases. *n.*

beach   [bēch]   **1** an almost flat shore of sand or little stones over which the water washes when high or at high tide. **2** run a boat ashore; draw up on the shore. 1 *n.*, 2 *v.*

beard   [bērd]   **1** the hair growing on a man's chin and cheeks. **2** face boldly; defy. 1 *n.*, 2 *v.*

beau·ti·ful   [byü′tə fəl]   very pleasing to see or hear; delighting the mind or senses. *adj.* —**beau·ti·ful·ly,** *adv.*

be·cause   [bi koz′ *or* bi kuz′]   for the reason that; since. *conj.*

be·gin·ning   [bi gin′ing]   **1** a start. **2** that begins; first in order. 1 *n.*, 2 *adj.*

be·lieve   [bi lēv′]   think something is true or real. *v.* **be·lieved, be·liev·ing.** —**be·liev′er,** *n.*

be·low   [bi lō′]   **1** in a lower place; to a lower place. **2** less than; lower in rank or degree than. **3** below zero on a Fahrenheit thermometer. 1 *adv.*, 2 *prep.*, 3 *adj.*

be·tween   [bi twēn′]   **1** in the space or time separating two points, objects, places, etc. **2** from one to the other of; joining; connecting. **3** by the joint action of. *prep.*
☛ *Usage.* **Between** is used when the following reference is to two persons or things only: *My sister and I had less than a dollar between us.* **Among** is usually preferred when the following reference is to more than two persons or things: *The money was divided among the four of us.*

biking shorts   [bī′king shôrts′]   tight, mid-length shorts for wear while cycling, made of a very strong stretchy material that supports the muscles while allowing freedom of movement. *n.*

bil·lion   [bil′yən]   a thousand million (1 000 000 000) in Canada, the United States, and France; a million million (1 000 000 000 000) in the United Kingdom. *n.* or *adj.*

bi·o·sphere   [bī′ə sfēr′]   the parts of the earth and its atmosphere in which living things are found. *n.*

birth   [bėrth]   **1** coming into life; being born. **2** a beginning. **3** bringing forth. **4** descent; family. *n.*
☛ *Homonyms.* **Birth** is pronounced like **berth**.

blur   [blėr]   **1** make confused in form or outline. **2** a blot; smear. 1 *v.*, **blurred, blur·ring;** 2, *n.*

board   [bôrd]   **1** a broad, thin piece of wood for use in building, etc. **2** cover with boards: *Father boards up the windows of our summer cottage in the fall.* **3** a flat piece of wood used for some special purpose. 1, 3 *n.*, 2 *v.*

bomb   [bom]   **1** a container filled with explosive that is exploded by a fuse or by the force with which it hits something. **2** attack with bombs. 1 *n.*, 2 *v.*
☛ *Homonyms.* **Bomb** is pronounced like **balm** [bom].

bore   [bôr]   **1** make a hole by means of a tool that keeps turning: *The workers dug the oil well by boring through the ground with huge drills.* **2** make weary by tiresome talk or by being dull. **3** a tiresome or dull person or thing. 1, 2 *v.*, **bored, bor·ing;** 3 *n.*

bot·tle [bot′əl] **1** a container for holding liquids, usually made of glass, having a narrow neck and no handles. **2** put into bottles. **1** *n.*, **2** *v.*, **bot·tled, bot·tling.**

bowl [bōl] **1** a hollow, rounded dish, usually without handles. **2** a large, heavy ball used in certain games. **3** play the game of bowling. **1, 2** *n.*, **3** *v.*

branch [branch] **1** part of a tree that grows out from the trunk. **2** a division; part: *a branch of a river.* **3** divide into branches: *The road branches at the bottom of the hill.* **1, 2** *n*, **3** *v.*

bright [brīt] **1** giving much light; shining. **2** very light or clear. **3** clever. *adj.* —**bright·ly,** *adv.* —**bright′ness,** *n.*

bril·liant [bril′yənt] **1** shining brightly; sparkling. **2** a diamond or other gem cut to sparkle brightly. **1** *adj.*, **2** *n.*

Brit·ish Co·lum·bi·a [brit′ish kə lum′bē ə] a province of western Canada.

broad·cast [brod′kast′] **1** send out by radio or television. **2** a radio or television program. **1** *v.*, **broad·cast** or (sometimes for def. 1) **broad·cast·ed, broad·cast·ing; 2** *n.* —**broad·cast′er,** *n.*

broc·co·flow·er [brok′ə flou′ər] a cross between broccoli and cauliflower, looking like bright green cauliflower. *n.*

bur·den [bėr′dən] **1** something carried; a load of things, duty, work, etc. **2** put a burden on; load. **1** *n.*, **2** *v.*

bur·y [ber′ē] **1** put a dead body in the earth, in a tomb, or in the sea. **2** put away; cover up; hide. *v.*, **bur·ied, bur·y·ing.**
☛ *Homonyms.* **Bury** is pronounced like berry.

C ▼▼▼

calling card [col′ing kärd′] a credit card issued by a phone company for making phone calls, especially when away from one's own phone. *n.*

call waiting [col′ wā′ ting] a feature of a telephone system allowing a single phone line to receive and hold calls while already in use. *n.*

calm [kom *or* käm] **1** quiet, still; not stormy or windy; not stirred up. **2** make calm; become calm. **1** *adj.*, **2** *v.* —**calm′ly,** *adv.* —**calm·ness,** *n.*

cal·zo·ne [kāl zō′nē] an Italian dish consisting of a pastry casing filled with meat, cheese, and vegetables. *n.*

cam·er·a [kam′ə rə] **1** a machine for taking photographs or motion pictures. **2** in television, a device to convert pictures into electrical impulses for transmitting. *n.*

hat, āge, fär; let, ēqual, tėrm; it, īce; hot, ōpen, ôrder
oil, out; cup, put, rüle; əbove, takən, pencəl, lemən, circəs
ch, child; ng, long; sh, ship
th, thin; ŦH, then; zh, measure

Ca·na·di·an [kə nā′dē ən] **1** a person born in or living in Canada. **2** of or having to do with Canada or its people. **1** *n.*, **2** *adj.*

ca·nal [kə nal′] waterway dug across land for ships or small boats to go through, or to carry water to places that need it. *n.*

ca·noe [kə nü′] **1** a light, narrow boat having sharp ends, moved with a paddle. **2** paddle a canoe; go in a canoe. **1** *n.*, *pl.*, **ca·noes; 2** *v.*, **ca·noed, ca·noe·ing.**

ca·pa·ble [ka′pə bəl] able; having fitness, power, or ability; efficient. *adj.*, —**ca′pa·bly,** *adv.*

cap·i·tal [kap′ə təl] **1** the city where the government of a country, province, or state is located. **2** a capital letter. **3** the amount of money or property that a company or a person uses in carrying on a business: *A great deal of capital is needed to set up an aluminum plant.* *n.*

care·free [ker′frē′] without worry; light-hearted; happy. *adj.*

care·ful [ker′fəl] thinking what one says; watching what one does; taking pains. *adj.* —**care′ful·ly,** *adv.* —**care′ful·ness,** *n.*

car·toon [kär tün′] **1** a sketch or drawing showing persons, things, or events in an amusing way. **2** a comic strip. *n.*

cen·tu·ry [sen′chə rē] **1** each 100 years, counting from some special time, such as the birth of Christ. **2** a period of 100 years: *From 1824 to 1924 is a century.* *n.*, *pl.* **cen·tu·ries.**

ce·re·al [sē′rē əl] **1** any grass that produces a grain which is used as a food: *Wheat, rice, corn, oats, and barley are cereals.* **2** the grain. *n.*

cer·tain·ly [sėr′tən lē] **1** surely; without doubt. **2** yes; of course. *adv.*

cham·pi·on [cham′pē ən] **1** a person, animal, or thing that wins first place in a game or contest. **2** first; ahead of all others. **3** a person who fights or speaks for another person; a person who defends a cause. **1, 3** *n.*, **2** *adj.*

change [chānj] **1** make different; become different. **2** a thing to be used in place of another of the same kind. **3** smaller units of money given in place of a large unit of money. **1** *v.*, **changed, chang·ing; 2, 3** *n.*

char·ac·ter [kar'ik tər *or* ker'ik tər]   **1** nature; kind; sort. **2** a person in a play or book. **3** a letter, figure, or sign used in writing, printing, or computing: *My computer keyboard has 64 characters including ten numerals [0–9], 26 alphabetic characters [A–Z], and 28 special characters.* *n.*

chart [chärt]   **1** a map. **2** a sheet of information arranged in pictures, diagrams, etc. **3** make a chart of. 1, 2 *n.*, 3 *v.*

check [chek]   **1** examine or compare to prove true or correct. **2** find out; investigate. *v.*
☛ *Homonyms.* **Check** is pronounced like **cheque**.

choc·o·late [chok'ə lit *or* chok'lit]   **1** a dark brown substance used as a food or flavouring and made by roasting and grinding cacao seeds. **2** made of or flavoured with chocolate. 1 *n.*, 2 *adj.*

choice [chois]   **1** choosing; selection. **2** a quantity and variety to choose from. *n.* **choic·er, choic·est.**

choose [chüz]   **1** pick out; select from a number. **2** prefer and decide. *v.*, **chose, cho·sen, choos·ing.**

chuck·le [chuk'əl]   **1** laugh to oneself. **2** a soft laugh; quiet laughter. 1 *v.*, **chuck·led, chuck·ling;** 2 *n.*

chun·nel [chun'əl]   the Chunnel tunnel between Great Britain and France. *n.*

chute [shüt]   **1** an inclined passage, trough, etc. down which things are dropped or slid to a lower level. **2** rapids in a river; waterfall. *n.*
☛ *Homonyms.* **Chute** is pronounced like **shoot**.

cit·y [sit'ē]   **1** a town of more than a certain size or level of importance. **2** the people living in a city. *n., pl.* **cit·ies.**

clip art [klip' ärt']   a bank of ready-made images that can be loaded into a computer. Any image can then be inserted into a document being written on the computer. *n.*

clip·board [klip'bôrd']   a small writing board having a heavy spring clip at one end for holding papers. *n.*

club·house [klub'hous']   a building used by a club. *n.*

coach [kōch]   **1** a person who teaches or trains athletes. **2** a private teacher who helps a student prepare for a special test. **3** train or teach: *He asked his mother to coach him in arithmetic.* 1, 2 *n.*, 3 *v.*

coarse [kôrs]   **1** made up of fairly large parts. **2** heavy or rough in looks or texture; not fine. *adj.* **coars·er, coars·est. —coarse'ly,** *adv..* **—coarse'ness,** *n.*
☛ *Homonyms.* **Coarse** is pronounced like **course**.

coast [kōst]   **1** the land along the sea; seashore. **2** ride down a hill without using effort or power. 1 *n.*, 2 *v.*

co·coa [kō'kō]   **1** a reddish brown powder made from chocolate by pressing out most of the fat. **2** a drink made from this powder with sugar and milk. *n.*
☛ *Homonyms.* **Cocoa** is pronounced like **coco**.

code [kōd]   **1** a collection of the laws of a country. **2** an arrangement of words or figures to keep a message short or secret; a system of secret writing. **3** a system of symbols for representing information in a computer. *n.*, **cod·ed, cod·ing.**

coin [koin]   **1** a piece of metal stamped by a government for use as money. **2** make up; invent: *to coin a new word or phrase* 1 *n.*, 2 *v.*

col·lect [kə lekt']   **1** gather together; pick up. **2** bring together into one place as a hobby. *v.*

col·li·sion [kə lizh'ən]   **1** a violent rushing against; hitting or striking hard together. **2** a clash; conflict. *n.*

com·bi·na·tion [kom'bə nā'shən]   **1** combining or being combined; union. **2** a series of numbers or letters followed in opening a certain kind of lock. *n.*

com·fort·a·ble [kum'fər tə bəl]   **1** giving a feeling of ease. **2** in comfort; at ease; free from pain or hardship. *adj.* **—com'fort·a·bly,** *adv.*

com·ic [kom'ik]   **1** amusing; funny. **2** comic strip. 1 *adj.*, 2 *n.*

com·pare [kəm per']   **1** find out or point out how persons or things are alike and how they are different. **2** be considered like or equal to. *v.*, **com·pared, com·par·ing.**

com·pete [kəm pet']   **1** try to do better than one or more other persons. **2** take part in a contest: *My brother competed in the swimming meet.* *v.*, **com·pet·ed, com·pet·ing.**

com·pe·ti·tion [kom'pə tish'ən]   **1** trying to do better than others; striving to excel. **2** a contest, especially one in which there is a prize for the winner. *n.*

com·plete [kəm plēt']   **1** with all the parts; whole; entire. **2** make whole or perfect; make up the full number or amount of. **3** finish. 1 *adj.*, 2, 3 *v.*, **com·plet·ed, com·plet·ing. —com·plete·ly,** *adv.*

com·po·si·tion [kom'pə zish'ən]   **1** the make-up of anything: *The composition of this candy includes sugar, chocolate, and milk.* **2** something composed, such as a piece of music, writing, etc. **3** a short essay written as a school exercise: *a composition about my dog.* *n.*

con·cen·tra·tion [kon'sən trā'shən]   **1** concentrating or being concentrated: *the concentration of all one's energy on a problem.* **2** close attention: *She gave the problem her full concentration.* *n.*

con·clude [kən clüd']   **1** finish; end. **2** reach or arrive at a decision or opinion by reasoning. *v.*, **con·clud·ed, con·clud·ing.**

con·clu·sion [kən klü′zhən] **1** an end. **2** the last main division of a speech, essay, etc. **3** a decision or opinion reached by reasoning. *n.*

con·di·tion [kən dish′ən] **1** the state in which a person or thing is; fitness. **2** put in good condition. **3** anything on which something else depends; something without which something else cannot exist: *Ability and effort are conditions of success.* 1, 3 *n.*, 2 *v.*
on condition that, if, provided that: *I'll go on condition that you will too.*

con·fer·ence [kon′fə rəns] a meeting of interested persons to discuss a particular subject. *n.*

con·fu·sion [kən fyü′zhən] **1** a mixed-up condition of things or of the mind. **2** the mistaking of one thing for another. **3** tumult: *After the home team won, the arena was a scene of utter confusion.* *n.*

con·nec·tion [kə nek′shən] **1** connecting or being connected. **2** any kind of particular relation with another thing. *n.*

con·serve [kən sėrv′ *for 1,* kon′sėrv *for 2*] **1** keep from harm or decay; keep from loss or from being used up; preserve. **2** fruit preserved in sugar; preserves; jam. 1 *v.*, **con·served, con·serv·ing;** 2 *n.*

con·sum·er [kən sü′mər *or* kən syü′mər] a person who uses food, clothing, or anything grown or made by producers. *n.*

con·tain·er [kən tā′nər] a box, can, jar, etc. used to hold something for storage or transport. *n.*

con·tent [kon′tent *for 1, 2,* kən tent′ *for 3*] **1** Usually, **contents,** *pl.* what is contained in anything; all things inside. **2** the facts or ideas stated; what is written in a book or said in a speech: *I could read her writing, but I couldn't understand the content of her essay.* **3** satisfy; please. 1, 2 *n.*, 3 *v.*
☞ *Usage.* **Content** refers mainly to the amount or quality of what is contained or included in something: *the content of a speech, argument, composition, etc.* **Contents** refers to the individual things contained in something: *the contents of a box.*

con·test [kon′test *for 1,* kən test′ *for 2*] **1** trial of skill to see who will win. **2** to dispute; struggle against; fight. 1 *n.*, 2 *v.*

con·tri·bu·tion [kon′trə byü′shən] **1** the act of giving money or help. **2** the money or help contributed; gift: *Her contribution to the picnic was a basket of apples.* **3** something written for a newspaper or magazine. *n.*

control pad [kən trōl′ pad] a hand-held unit for playing video games. It combines a directional control, which functions like a joystick, and action buttons for shooting etc. *n.*

hat, āge, fär; let, ēqual, tėrm; it, īce; hot, ōpen, ôrder oil, out; cup, pùt, rüle; əbove, takən, pencəl, lemən, circəs
ch, child; ng, long; sh, ship
th, thin; ᴛʜ, then; zh, measure

con·ver·sa·tion [kon′vər sā′shən] friendly talk; the exchange of thoughts by talking informally together. *n.*

con·vert [kən vėrt′ *for 1 and 2,* kon′vėrt *for 3*] **1** change; turn. **2** cause to change from one belief or way of thinking to another. **3** a person who has been converted. 1, 2 *v.*, 3 *n.*

co–op·er·ate [kō op′ə rāt′] work together. *v.*, **co-op·er·at·ed, co-op·er·at·ing.**

cop·y [kop′ē] **1** anything made to be just like another; anything made on the model of another. **2** make a copy of. 1 *n., pl.* **cop·ies;** 2 *v.,* **cop·ied, cop·y·ing.**

course [kôrs] **1** an onward movement. **2** the regular order; the ordinary way of proceeding. *n.* **coursed, cours·ing.**

coy·ote [kī′ōt, kī′ùt, *or* kī ō′tē] a North American wild animal related to the dog, having yellow or yellowish grey fur and noted for the way it howls at night. *n., pl.* **coy·otes** *or* **coy·ote.**

craft [kraft] **1** skill. **2** a trade or art requiring skilled work. **3** skill in deceiving others; sly tricks. *n.*

cra·ter [krā′tər] **1** the opening at the top of a volcano. **2** a big hole shaped like a bowl. *n.*

cre·ate [krē āt′] **1** make a thing that has not existed before. **2** make something original by intelligence and skill: *This garden was created from a gravel quarry.* *v.,* **cre·at·ed, cre·at·ing.**

crea·ture [krē′chər] any living person or animal. *n.*

cred·it [kred′it] **1** belief in the truth of something; faith; trust: *One cannot be blamed for placing little credit in the words of a liar.* **2** add to an account as a deposit. 1 *n.,* 2 *v.*

creep [krēp] **1** move slowly with the body close to the ground or floor; crawl: *A baby learns to creep before it learns to walk.* **2** creeping; a slow movement. 1 *v.,* 2 *n.* **crept, creep·ing.**

crime [krīm] a deed that is against the law; an illegal act. *n.*

cross trainers [kros′ trā′nərz] running shoes designed for a variety of mainly outdoor athletic activities having a relatively deep tread. *n.*

crouch [krouch] **1** stoop low with bent legs like an animal ready to spring, or like a person hiding. **2** a crouching position. 1 *v.,* 2 *n.*

crys·tal [kris′təl] **1** a clear, transparent mineral, a kind of quartz, that looks like ice. **2** a piece of crystal cut to a form for use or ornament. **3** transparent glass of good quality. *n.*

cul·ture [kul′chər] **1** the customs and arts of a nation or people at a certain time. **2** the preparation of land and production of crops. *n.*

cu·ri·ous [kyü′rē əs] **1** eager to know. **2** strange; odd; unusual. *adj.*

cur·ren·cy [kėr′ən sē] the money in actual use in a country. *n., pl.* **cur·ren·cies.**

cush·ion [kush′ən] **1** a soft pillow or pad for a chesterfield, chair, etc., used to sit, lie, or kneel on. **2** supply with a cushion. **1** *n.,* **2** *v.*

D ▼▼▼

dark·en [där′kən] make dark or darker; become dark or darker. *v.*

data base [dā′tə bās′ *or* dat′ə bās′] information stored and available for processing in a computer. *n.*

daz·zle [daz′əl] **1** hurt the eyes with too bright a light, or with quick-moving lights. **2** a dazzling, bewildering, brightness. **1** *v.,* **daz·zled, daz·zling; 2** *n.*

del·i·cate [del′ə kit] **1** gently pleasing the sense; mild; soft. **2** of fine weave, quality, or make; thin; easily broken. *adj.*

de·li·cious [di lish′əs] very pleasing or satisfying; delightful, especially to taste or smell: *a delicious cake. adj.* —**de·li′cious·ly,** *adv.*

den·tist [den′tist] a person who is qualified to work in the prevention and treatment of tooth decay and other problems and diseases of the teeth and gums. *n.*

de·ny [di nī′] **1** say that something is not true. **2** say that one does not hold to or believe in. **3** refuse. *v.,* **de·nied, de·ny·ing.**

de·part·ment [di pärt′mənt] a separate part of some whole; special branch; division. *n.*

depth [depth] **1** the distance from the top to the bottom. **2** the distance from front to back. **3** the deepest or most central part of anything. *n.*
out of one's depth, a in water so deep that one cannot touch the bottom. **b** in a situation too difficult to understand or cope with: *He was out of his depth in the arithmetic class.*

des·per·ate [des′pə rit] **1** having lost all hope. **2** having an extreme need or desire. *adj.*

de·stroy [di stroi′] **1** break to pieces; spoil; ruin; make useless. **2** put an end to; do away with. *v.*

de·tec·tive [di tek′tiv] **1** a police officer whose work is investigating crime. **2** a person who works for a company or organization as an investigator. *n.*

di·al [dī′əl *or* dīl] **1** the circular device on many telephones that is rotated for signalling the required telephone number when making a call. **2** make a call by means of a telephone dial. **1** *n.,* **2** *v.,* **di·alled** or **di·aled, di·al·ling** or **di·al·ing.**

dia·mond [dī′ə mənd *or* dī′mənd] **1** a colourless or tinted precious stone, formed of pure carbon in crystals. **2** a figure shaped like this: ◆. *n.*

dif·fer·ent [dif′ə rənt] **1** not alike; not like. **2** not the same; separate; distinct. *adv.*

dig·it·al [dij′ə təl] **1** of or having to do with the fingers or toes. **2** of or having to do with numerals (digits) or calculation by numerals. **3** of, having to do with, or providing information in the form of numerals: *A digital clock shows the time in the form of changing numerals rather than by hands moving over a dial. adj.*

di·men·sion [di men′shən *or* dī men′shən] **1** the measurement of length, breadth, or thickness. **2** Usually, **dimensions,** *pl.* size; extent; scope. *n.*

di·rec·tor [di rek′tər *or* dī rek′tər] a manager; a person who directs. *n.*

dirt·y [dėr′tē] **1** not clean; soiled by mud, dust, earth, or anything like them. **2** make dirty; soil. **1** *adj.,* **dirt·i·er, dirt·i·est; 2** *v.,* **dirt·ied, dirt·y·ing.**

dis·a·gree [dis′ə grē′] **1** fail to agree; be different. **2** having unlike opinions; differ. *v.,* **dis·a·greed, dis·a·gree·ing.**

dis·ap·point [dis′ə point′] fail to satisfy one's desire, wish, or hope. *v.*

dis·cour·age [dis kėr′ij] **1** take away the courage of; destroy the hopes of. **2** try to prevent by disapproving; frown upon. *v.,* **dis·cour·aged, dis·cour·ag·ing.**

dis·grace [dis grās′] **1** a loss of respect or honour. **2** cause to lose honour; dishonour; bring shame upon. **1** *n.,* **2** *v.,* **dis·graced, dis·grac·ing.**

dis·grace·ful [dis grās′fəl] shameful; causing dishonour or loss of respect; deserving disgrace. *adj.* —**dis·grace′ful·ly,** *adv.*

dis·hon·est [di son′ist] **1** unfair; not fair. **2** not honest. *adj.*

dis·play [dis plā′] **1** show; reveal. **2** showing; exhibition. **1** *v.,* **2** *n.*

dis·tance [dis′təns] **1** the space in between. **2** a long way; far away. *n.*
in the distance, a long way off: *The sailors saw a light in the distance.*

di·vide [di vīd′] **1** separate into parts. **2** in mathematics, show a number as separated into equal parts by a smaller number. *v.* **di·vid·ed, di·vid·ing.**

does·n't [duz′ənt] does not.

dol·lar [dol′ər]   1 the unit of money in Canada, the United States, and some other countries.   2 a paper note or a coin worth 100 cents: *He gave me four quarters for a dollar. His mother gave him a silver dollar. n.*

do·mes·tic [də mes′tik]   1 of the home, household, or family affairs.   2 of or made in one's own country; not foreign. *adj.*

dou·ble [dub′əl]   1 twice as much, as large, as strong, etc.   2 become twice as much. 1 *adj.*, 2 *v.*

doubt [dout]   1 not believe; not be sure; feel uncertain.   2 difficulty in believing. 1 *v.*, 2 *n.*

drag [drag]   1 pull or move along heavily or slowly; pull or drag along the ground.   2 go too slowly. *v.* **dragged, drag·ging.**

dra·mat·ic [drə mat′ik]   1 of drama; having to do with plays.   2 sudden; exciting; full of action or feeling. *adj.*

drown [droun]   1 die under water or some other liquid because of lack of air to breathe.   2 be stronger or louder than; keep from being heard. *v.*

dub [dub]   1 add music, voices, or sound effects to (a film, a radio or television broadcast, a recording, etc.) by making or replacing a sound track: *The Italian film was dubbed with English dialogue.* 2 add (sounds) to a film, recording, etc. *v.*

dwarf [dwôrf]   1 an animal, or a plant much smaller than the usual size for its kind.   2 in fairy tales, a tiny, often ugly, person who has magic powers.   3 below the usual size for its kind; stopped in growth. 1, 2 *n., pl.* **dwarfs** or **dwarves** [dwôrvz]; 3 *adj.*

E ▼▼▼

earth·quake [ėrth′kwāk′]   a moving of the earth's crust. Earthquakes are caused by movements far below the surface and are sometimes violent enough to destroy buildings, roads, etc. *n.*

ed·i·ble [ed′ə bəl]   fit to eat; eatable: *Not all mushrooms are edible. adj.*

ed·it [ed′it]   1 prepare for publication, correcting errors, checking facts, etc.   2 have charge of a newspaper, magazine, dictionary, or a section of it. *v.*

Ed·mon·ton [ed′mən tən]   the capital city of Alberta, Canada.

ed·u·ca·tion [ej′u kā′shən]   1 a development of knowledge and skills by teaching or study.   2 the knowledge and abilities gained through training. *n.*

ef·fec·tive [i fek′tiv]   1 able to cause some desired result.   2 in operation; active. *adj.*

hat, āge, fär; let, ēqual, tėrm; it, īce; hot, ōpen, ôrder oil, out; cup, pùt, rüle; ə above, takən, pencəl, lemən, circəs ch, child; ng, long; sh, ship th, thin; ᴛʜ, then; zh, measure

e·lab·o·rate [i lab′ə rit *for 1,* i lab′ə rāt′ *for 2*]   1 worked out with great care; having many details; complicated.   2 work out with great care; add details to: *The inventor spent months in elaborating plans for a new engine.* 1 *adj.*, 2 *v.*, **e·lab·o·rat·ed, e·lab·o·rat·ing.**

em·er·ald [em′ə rəld]   1 a clear bright-green precious stone.   2 bright green. 1, 2 *n.*, 2 *adj.*

e·mis·sion [ē mi′shən]   the act of sending forth: *The emission of fumes from the car's exhaust clouded the garage. n.*

em·ploy [em ploi′]   1 give work and pay to.   2 use. *v.*

end·less [end′lis]   1 having no end; never stopping; lasting or going on forever.   2 appearing to have no end; seeming never to stop. *adj.*

Eng·lish [ing′glish]   1 the people of England.   2 the language of England and many other countries. *n.*

en·joy·a·ble [en joi′ə bəl]   pleasant; giving joy. *adj.*

e·ro·sion [i rō′zhən]   the process of being worn away gradually. *n.*

e·rupt [i rupt′]   1 burst forth.   2 break out in a rash. *v.*

es·cape [es kāp′]   1 get free; get out and away.   2 the act of escaping. 1 *v.*, 2 *n.* **es·caped, es·cap·ing.**

ex·cel·lent [ek′sə lənt]   exceptionally good. *adj.*

ex·cept [ek sept′]   1 leaving out; other than.   2 leave out: *The teacher excepted them from the examination list.* 1 *prep.*, 2 *v.*

ex·change [eks chānj′]   1 give for something else.   2 give in trade for something regarded as of equal value. *v.*, **ex·changed, ex·chang·ing.**

ex·cite [ek sīt′]   1 stir up the feelings of.   2 stir to action. *v.*, **ex·cit·ed, ex·cit·ing.**

ex·claim [ek sklām′]   cry out; speak suddenly in surprise, strong feeling, etc. *v.*

ex·hi·bi·tion [ek′sə bish′ən]   1 display.   2 a public show. *n.*

ex·pand [ek spand′]   1 increase in size; enlarge; swell.   2 spread out; open out; unfold; extend. *v.*

ex·pen·sive [ek spen′siv]   costly; high-priced. *adj.*

179

ex·pe·ri·ence [ek spē′rē əns] **1** what happens to a person. **2** practice; knowledge gained by doing or seeing things. *n.,* **ex·pe·ri·enced, ex·pe·ri·enc·ing.**

ex·per·i·ment [ek sper′ə ment′ *for 1,* ek sper′ə mənt *for 2*] **1** try in order to find out; make trials or tests. **2** a trial or test to find out something: *a cooking experiment, a scientific experiment.* 1 *v.,* 2 *n.*

ex·pert [ek′spėrt] **1** a person who has much skill or who knows a great deal about some special thing. **2** having much skill; knowing a great deal about some special thing. 1 *n.,* 2 *adj.*

ex·plain [ek splān′] **1** make plain or clear; tell the meaning of; tell how to do. **2** state the cause of; give reasons for. *v.*

ex·plore [ek splôr′] **1** go or travel over land, water, or through space for the purpose of finding out about geographical features, natural resources, etc. **2** go over carefully; examine. *v.,* **ex·plored, ex·plor·ing.**

ex·plo·sion [ek splō′zhən] **1** a blowing up; a bursting with a loud noise. **2** a loud noise caused by something blowing up. *n.*

ex·tra [ek′strə] **1** beyond what is usual, expected, or needed. **2** anything that is extra. **3** more than usually; especially; *extra fine quality, an extra fast race.* 1 *adj.,* 2 *n.,* 3 *adv.*

ex·treme [ek strēm′] **1** much more than usual, very great; very strong. **2** at the very end; the farthest possible; last: *I know the person on the extreme right of that group.* *adj.* —**ex·treme·ly,** *adv.*

F ▼▼▼

fac·to·ry [fak′tə rē] **1** a building or group of buildings where things are manufactured. **2** in former times, a trading post. *n., pl.* **fac·to·ries.**

fail·ure [fāl′yər] **1** a falling short of success; lack of success. **2** the fact of not getting a passing mark in a test, examination, or course in school. *n.*

fa·la·fel [fə lä′ fəl] a Middle Eastern dish of seasoned, fried chick peas and other vegetables stuffed into the pocket of a pita. *n.*

fan·ta·sy [fan′tə sē] **1** the imagination; the play of the mind. **2** wild imagining; fanciful thinking. *n., pl.* **fan·ta·sies.**

far·ther [fär′ᴛʜər] more distant; a greater distance. *adj.*

fash·ion [fash′ən] **1** the current custom in dress, manners, speech, etc.; style. **2** make, shape, or form. 1 *n.,* 2 *v.*

feath·er [feᴛʜ′ər] **1** one of the light, thin growths that cover a bird's skin. **2** supply or cover with feathers. 1 *n.,* 2 *v.*

fer·tile [fėr′tīl *or* fėr′təl] **1** capable of bearing seeds, fruit, or young. **2** of soil, capable of producing plants, crops, etc. *adj.*

fierce [fērs] **1** savage; wild: *a fierce lion.* **2** raging; violent: *a fierce wind.* **3** very eager or active; ardent: *a fierce determination to win.*

fig·ure [fig′ər *or* fig′yər] **1** use numbers to find out the answer to some problem. **2** a person considered from the point of view of appearance, manner, etc. 1 *v.,* 2 *n.* **fig·ured, fig·ur·ing.**

film [film] **1** cover or become covered with a film. **2** a roll or sheet of thin material covered with a special coating and used to take photographs. 1 *v.,* 2 *n.*

fit [fit] **1** having the necessary qualities; right; suitable. **2** healthy and strong. **3** make the right size and shape; adjust. 1, 2 *adj.,* **fit·ter, fit·test;** 3 *v.,* **fit·ted, fit·ting;** —**fit′ness,** *n.*

flute [flüt] **1** a long, slender wind instrument, played by blowing across a hole near one end. Different tones are made on a flute by opening and closing holes along the tube with the fingers or with keys. **2** play on a flute. 1 *n.,* 2 *v.,* **flut·ed, flut·ing.**

fool [fül] **1** a person without sense; a person who acts in a senseless and unreasonable way. **2** act like a fool for fun; play; joke. **3** make a fool of; deceive; trick. 1 *n.,* 2, 3 *v.*

foot·ball [fùt′bol′] **1** an outdoor game played by two teams, in which each side tries to kick, pass, or carry a ball across the opposing team's goal line. **2** the oval, air-filled, usually leather ball used in playing this game. **3** *British.* soccer. *n.*

force·ful [fôrs′fəl] having much force; forcible; effective; vigorous; strong: *She is a quiet but forceful speaker.* *adj.*

for·get [fər get′] **1** let go out of the mind; fail to remember. **2** leave behind unintentionally. *v.,* **for·got, for·got·ten** or **for·got, for·get·ting.**

for·mu·la [fôr′myə lə] **1** a recipe; prescription. **2** a mixture, especially one for feeding a baby, made according to a recipe or prescription. *n.*

for·tu·nate [fôr′chə nit] **1** having good luck; lucky. **2** bringing good luck; having favourable results: *a fortunate event.* *adj.*

for·ward [fôr′wərd] **1** onward; ahead. **2** in certain games, a player whose position is in the front line. 1 *adv.,* 2 *n.*

fos·sil [fos′əl] **1** the remains of prehistoric animals or plants preserved in rocks where they have become petrified. **2** traces of animal life preserved in ancient rocks. *n.*

foul [foul] **1** very dirty; impure; nasty. **2** unfair, against the rules. *adj.*
☛ *Homonyms.* **Foul** is pronounced like fowl.

180

fourth [fôrth] **1** next after the 3rd; last in a series of four; 4th. **2** a quarter; one, or being one, of four equal parts: *Twenty-five cents is one fourth of a dollar.* *adj.* or *n.*

frag·ment [frag′mənt] a part broken off; a piece of something broken. *n.*

freight [frāt] **1** the goods that a ship or a train carries. **2** the price paid for carrying. *n.*

French [french] **1** the people of France. **2** of or having to do with France, its people, or their language. **1** *n.*, **2** *adj.*

friend·ly [frend′lē] **1** like a friend; like a friend's. **2** on good terms. *adj.*, **friend·li·er, friend·li·est.** —**friend′li·ness,** *n.*

fright·en [frī′tən] make afraid. *v.*

fund [fund] **1** a sum of money set aside for a special purpose. **2** a stock or supply ready for use. **3 funds,** *pl.* money ready to use. *n.*

fu·ri·ous [fyu̇′rē əs] **1** raging; violent. **2** full of wild, fierce anger: *My father was furious when he learned of the broken window.* *adj.*

G ▼▼▼

ga·rage [gə räzh′, gə raj′ *or* gə razh′] **1** a place for keeping automobiles. **2** a service station. *n.*

gar·ment [gär′mənt] any article of clothing. *n.*

gen·tly [jent′lē] **1** in a gentle way; tenderly; softly. **2** gradually: *a gently sloping hillside.* *adv.*

gi·ant [jī′ənt] **1** a person of great size or very great power. **2** an imaginary being who is huge and powerful. **3** huge: *a giant potato.* **1, 2** *n.*, **3** *adj.*

glass [glas] **1** a hard substance that breaks easily and can usually be seen through. **2** cover or protect with glass. **1** *n.*, **2** *v.*

glit·ter [glit′ər] **1** glisten; sparkle; shine with a bright, sparkling light. **2** a bright, sparkling light. **1** *v.*, **2** *n.*

goal·ie [gō′lē] the player who guards the goal to prevent scoring in such games as hockey, lacrosse, etc. *n.*

grab [grab] **1** seize suddenly; snatch. **2** a snatching; a sudden seizing. **1** *v.*, **grabbed, grab·bing; 2** *n.*

grand [grand] **1** fine; noble; dignified; stately; splendid. **2** great; important; main: *the grand staircase.* *adj.*

groove [grüv] **1** a long, narrow channel or furrow, especially one cut by a tool. **2** make a groove in. **1** *n.*, **2** *v.*, **grooved, groov·ing.**

growth [grōth] **1** the process of growing; development. **2** the amount grown; increase; progress. *n.*

hat, āge, fär; let, ēqual, tėrm; it, īce; hot, ōpen, ôrder oil, out; cup, pu̇t, rüle; ə above, takən, pencəl, lemən, circəs ch, child; ng, long; sh, ship th, thin; ᴛʜ, then; zh, measure

H ▼▼▼

half [haf] **1** one of two equal parts. **2** making a half of; needing as much more to make a whole. **1** *n.*, *pl.* **halves; 2** *adj.*

hap·pen [hap′ən] **1** take place; occur. **2** be or take place by chance. *v.*

hard·ly [härd′lē] **1** only just; barely. **2** not quite; not altogether. *adv.*

harm [härm] **1** hurt; damage. **2** hurt or damage. **1** *n.*, **2** *v.* —**harm′ful,** *adj.* —**harm′less,** *adj.*

has·n't [haz′ənt] has not.

heard [hėrd] the past tense and past participle of hear. *v.*
☛ *Homonyms.* **Heard** is pronounced like **herd.**

heav·y [hev′ē] **1** hard to lift or carry; having much mass. **2** weighted down; laden. *adj.*, **heav·i·er, heav·i·est.**

he'd [hēd] **1** he had. **2** he would.
☛ *Homonyms.* **He'd** is pronounced like **heed.**

he·li·ski·ing [hel′ ə skē′ ing] a kind of skiing in which the skier is dropped by helicopter at the top of a slope and skis down. It is often done on a remote slope not specially prepared for skiing, in which case it must be above the treeline. *n.*

hid·den [hid′ən] **1** put or kept out of sight; secret; not clear: *Her speech was full of hidden meanings.* **2** a past participle of **hide:** *The moon was hidden behind a dark cloud.* **1** *adj.*, **2** *v.*

high·land [hī′lənd] **1** a country or region that is higher and hillier than the neighbouring country. **2 the Highlands,** a hilly region in northern and western Scotland. *n.*

his·to·ry [his′tə rē] **1** a statement of what has happened. **2** the story of a person or a nation. *n.*, *pl.* **his·to·ries.**

hol·o·gram [hol′ə gram] *Optics.* a three-dimensional photograph obtained by exposing a photographic plate near an object illuminated by a laser beam. *n.*

home page [hōm′ pāj′] the first page or file reached at any given address on the World Wide Web. *n.*

hope·less [hōp′lis] **1** feeling no hope. **2** giving no hope: *When everything went wrong, it became a hopeless situation.* *adj.*

hu·mor·ous [hyü′mə rəs] full of humour; funny; amusing: *a humorous story.* *adj.*

hur·ry [hėr′ē] **1** drive, carry, send, or move quickly. **2** a hurried movement or action. 1 *v.*, **hur·ried, hur·ry·ing;** 2 *n., pl.* **hur·ries.**

hy·dro·foil [hī′drə foil′] **1** one of a set of blades or fins attached to the hull of a boat at an angle so that the boat, when moving, is lifted just clear of the water. Hydrofoils reduce friction and thus increase speed. **2** a boat equipped with hydrofoils. *n.*

I ▼▼▼

ig·no·rant [ig′nə rənt] **1** knowing little or nothing; without knowledge. **2** caused by or showing lack of knowledge. *adj.*

ig·nore [ig nôr′] pay no attention to; disregard. *v.*, **ig·nored, ig·nor·ing.**

il·lus·trate [il′əs trāt′] **1** make clear or explain by stories, examples, comparisons, etc. **2** provide with pictures, diagrams, maps, etc. that explain or decorate. *v.*, **il·lus·trat·ed, il·lus·trat·ing.**

im·age [im′ij] **1** a likeness or copy. **2** a picture in the mind. **3** make or form an image of. 1, 2 *n.*, 3 *v.*, **im·aged, im·ag·ing.**

i·mag·ine [i maj′ən] **1** picture in one's mind; form an image or idea of. **2** suppose; guess. *v.*, **i·mag·ined, i·mag·in·ing.**

im·por·tant [im pôr′tənt] **1** meaning much; having value or significance. **2** having special authority, social position, or influence. *adj.* —**im·por′tant·ly,** *adv.*

im·pos·si·ble [im pos′ə bəl] **1** that cannot be done. **2** that cannot be true. *adj.* —**im·pos′si·bly,** *adv.*

im·pres·sive [im pres′iv] making an impression on the mind, feelings, conscience, etc.: *an impressive ceremony. The view was very impressive. adj.* —**im·pres′sive·ly,** *adv.*

in·de·pend·ent [in′di pen′dənt] **1** not needing, wanting, or getting help from others; not connected with others. **2** a person who is independent in thought or behaviour. 1 *adj.*, 2 *n.* —**in′de·pend′ent·ly,** *adv.*

in·dus·try [in′dəs trē] **1** any branch of business, trade, or manufacture. **2** the production of goods; manufacturing in general. *n., pl.* **in·dus·tries.**

in·field [in′fēld′] **1** the part of a baseball field within the base lines; diamond. **2** the first, second, and third base players and shortstop of a baseball team. *n.*

in·fo·mer·cial [in′fō mėr′ shəl] a television program which consists entirely of long advertisements. *n.*

in·gre·di·ent [in grē′dē ənt] one of the parts of a mixture. *n.*

in·ju·ry [in′jə rē] **1** a hurt or loss caused to or endured by a person or thing; harm; damage. **2** unfairness; injustice; wrong. *n., pl.* **in·ju·ries.**

in·stant [in′stənt] **1** a particular moment. **2** immediate. 1 *n.*, 2 *adj.*

in·struc·tion [in struk′shən] **1** teaching or lessons. **2 instructions,** *pl.* orders. *n.*

interactive TV [in′ tər āk′tiv tē′ vē] television in which the viewer can partly control what appears on the screen, such as by choosing to show an instant replay or the view from a particular camera angle. *n.*

in·ter·change [in′tər chānj′ *for 1*, in′tər chānj′ *for 2*] **1** put each of two or more persons or things in the other's place. **2** a road that permits traffic from one highway to change to another without crossing in front of other traffic; cloverleaf. 1 *v.*, **in·ter·changed, in·ter·chang·ing;** 2 *n.*

in·ter·fere [in′tər fēr′] **1** clash; come into opposition with. **2** disturb the affairs of others; meddle. *v.*, **in·ter·fered, in·ter·fer·ing.**

in·ter·na·tion·al [in′tər nash′ə nəl *or* in′tər nash′nəl] **1** between or among nations. **2** having to do with the relations between nations. *adj.* —**in′ter·na′tion·al·ly,** *adv.*

in·ter·rupt [in′tə rupt′] **1** break in upon talk, work, rest, a person speaking, etc.; hinder; stop. **2** cause a break; break in. *v.*

in·ter·view [in′tər vyü′] **1** meeting in person to talk over something special. **2** meet and talk with, especially to obtain information: *Reporters from the newspaper interviewed the returning astronauts.* 1 *n.*, 2 *v.*, —**in′ter·view′er,** *n.*

in·tro·duc·tion [in′trə duk′shən] **1** an introducing. **2** something that introduces; the first part of a book, speech, piece of music, etc. leading up to the main part. *n.*

in·va·sion [in vā′zhen] **1** the act or fact of invading; entering by force. **2** an interference or intrusion. *n.*

in·ven·tion [in ven′shən] **1** making something new. **2** the thing invented. *n.*

ir·ri·gate [ir′ə gāt′] **1** supply land with water by means of ditches, sprinklers, etc. **2** supply or wash a wound, cavity in the body, etc. with a continuous flow of some liquid. *v.*, **ir·ri·gat·ed, ir·ri·gat·ing.**

i·tem [ī′təm] **1** a separate thing or article: *The list had twelve items on it.* **2** a piece of news; a bit of information: *There were several interesting items in today's paper. n.*

J ▼▼▼

join [join] **1** bring or put together; connect, fasten, or clasp together. **2** come together; meet. *v.*

joy·stick [joi′ stik′] *Computer technology.* a computer input device in which the movement of a small lever causes a corresponding movement of an object or cursor on the screen. *n.*

juicy [jü′ sē] full of juice; having much juice: *a juicy orange.* *adj.*, **juic·i·er, juic·i·est.**

K

knee [nē] **1** the joint between the thigh and the lower leg. **2** strike with the knee. 1 *n.*, 2 *v.*, **kneed, knee·ing.**

knew [nyü *or* nü] the past tense of **know**: *She knew the right answer.* *v.*
☛ *Homonyms.* **Knew** is pronounced like **new.**

knock [nok] **1** give a hard blow or blows to with the fist, knuckles, or anything hard; hit. **2** the sound of knocking: *The knock on the door made us all jump.* 1 *v.*, 2 *n.*

L ▼▼▼

lar·va [lär′və] **1** the early form of an insect from the time it leaves the egg until it becomes a pupa. **2** a young form of certain animals that is different in structure from the adult form. *n.*, *pl.* **lar·vae** [lär′vē].

lav·a [lav′ə *or* lä′və] **1** hot melted rock flowing from a volcano. **2** rock formed by the cooling of this melted rock. Some lavas are hard and glassy while others are light and porous. *n.*

league [lēg] **1** a union of persons, parties, or nations formed to help one another. **2** a group of teams that play a schedule of games against each other. **3** form a league. 1, 2 *n.*, 3 *v.*, **leagued, lea·guing.**

les·son [les′ən] **1** a unit of teaching of learning; what is to be studied or taught at one time. **2** an instructive experience, serving to encourage or warn: *The accident was a lesson to me.* *n.*

let·ter [let′ər] **1** a symbol or sign, used alone or combined, that represents speech sounds; a character of an alphabet. **2** a written or printed message. *n.*

li·brar·y [lī′ brer′ē] a room or building where a collection of books, magazines, phonograph records, etc. is kept to be used, rented, or borrowed. *n.*, *pl.* **lib·rar·ies.**

lift [lift] **1** raise; raise up higher; raise into the air; take up; pick up. **2** rise and go; go away. *v.*

lis·ten [lis′ən] **1** try to hear; make an effort so as to hear. **2** give head to advice, temptation, etc.; pay attention: *I don't know how to repair it because I did not listen.* *v.* **—lis′ten·er,** *n.*

lock [lok] **1** means of fastening doors, boxes, etc. usually needing a key or special shape to open it. **2** fasten with a lock. **3** shut something in or out or up. 1 *n.*, 2, 3 *v.*

hat, āge, fär; let, ēqual, tėrm; it, īce; hot, ōpen, ôrder oil, out; cup, pùt, rüle; əbove, takən, pencəl, lemən, circəs ch, child; ng, long; sh, ship th, thin; ᴛʜ, then; zh, measure

lone·ly [lōn′lē] **1** feeling oneself alone and longing for company or friends. **2** without many people. *adj.*, **lone·li·er, lone·li·est.**

lose [lüz] **1** not have any longer; have taken away from one by accident, carelessness, parting, death, etc. **2** fail to win. *v.*, **lost, los·ing.** **—los′er,** *n.*

loud·speak·er [loud′spē kər] a device that changes an electric signal into sound, as in a radio or public address system. The sound can be made louder by increasing the strength of the electric signal. *n.*

love·ly [luv′lē] **1** beautiful in appearance or character; lovable. **2** *Informal.* very pleasing; delightful. *adj.*, **love·li·er, love·li·est.**

luckily [luk′ə lē] by good luck; fortunately. *adv.*

M ▼▼▼

maintain [mān tān′] **1** keep; keep up; carry on. **2** keep in good repair. *v.*
☛ *Etymology.* **Maintain** comes from French but goes back to a Latin phrase meaning 'hold by the hand'.

man·ag·er [man′i jər] a person who manages, especially one who manages a business: *a store manager.* *n.*

man·u·fac·ture [man′yə fak′chər] **1** to make by hand or machine. **2** the making of something by hand or by machine, especially in large quantities. 1 *v.*, **man·u·fac·tured, man·u·fac·tur·ing;** 2 *n.*

mar·riage [mar′ij *or* mer′ij] **1** married life; living together as husband and wife. **2** the ceremony of being married; a wedding. *n.*

me·di·a [mē′dē ə] a plural of **medium**: *Newspapers, magazines, and billboards are important media for advertising.* *n.*

mes·sage [mes′ij] information or instructions sent from one person to another: *a message of welcome, a radio message.* *n.*

meth·od [meth′əd] **1** a way of doing something. **2** order or system in getting things done or in thinking: *If you used more method, you wouldn't waste so much time.* *n.*

Mex·i·can [mek′sə kən] **1** a person born in or living in Mexico. **2** of or having to do with Mexico or its people. 1 *n.*, 2 *adj.*

mi·cro·pro·ces·sor [mīk′ rō prō′ ses ər] *or* [mīk′ rō pros′ es ər] *Computer technology.* an integrated circuit consisting of usually a single chip of semiconductor that carries out instructions in a computer or other electronic device. *n.*

mi·grate   [mī'grāt *or* mī grāt']   **1** move from one place to settle in another. **2** go from one region to another with the change in the seasons: *Many birds migrate to warmer regions in the winter. v.,* **mi·grat·ed, mi·grat·ing.**

min·er·al   [min'ə rəl]   **1** a substance obtained by mining or digging in the earth. **2** any natural substance that is neither plant nor animal. *n.*

min·i–ser·ies   [min' ē sēr' ēz]   a television drama in serial form. *n.*

miss   [mis]   **1** fail to hit. **2** a failure to hit or reach. **3** let slip by. **1, 3** *v.,* **2** *n.*

mist   [mist]   **1** a cloud of very fine drops or water in the air; fog. **2** come down in mist; rain in very fine drops. **1** *n.,* **2** *v.*

molt·en   [mōl'tən]   made liquid by heat; melted. *adj.*

mo·ment   [mō'mənt]   **1** a very short space of time; an instant. **2** a particular point of time. *n.*

mountain bike   [moun'tən bīk']   a sturdy bicycle with straight handlebars, for riding anywhere including rough terrain. It has wider tires with deeper treads than a racer and usually, a more comfortable seat. *n.*

mul·ti·ply   [mul'tə plī']   **1** take a number or quantity a given number of times. **2** increase in number or amount: *The dangers and difficulties multiplied as we went higher up the mountain. v.,* **mul·ti·plied, mul·ti·ply·ing.**

mul·ti·me·di·a   [mul' tē mē' dē ə]   using, involving, or including several media together: *a multimedia sales presentation, a multimedia art exhibition.*

mu·si·cian   [myü zish'ən]   a person skilled in music, especially one who earns a living by singing, playing, composing, or conducting music. *n.*

mus·tache   [mus'tash or mə stash']   the hair that grows on a man's upper lip, especially when allowed to grow into a shape such as a curve. *n.*

mys·ter·i·ous   [mis tē'rē əs]   **1** full of mystery; hard to explain or understand; secret; hidden. **2** suggesting mystery: *a mysterious look. adj.*

N ▼▼▼

na·tion   [nā'shən]   **1** a group of people occupying the same country, united under the same independent government, and, usually, speaking the same language. **2** a people, race, or tribe; those having the same descent, history, and, as a rule, language. **3** such a group considered as a political unity. *n.*

nec·es·sar·y   [nes'ə ser'ē]   **1** that must be, be had, or be done; required. **2** something essential; something that cannot be done without: *Food, clothing, and shelter are necessaries of life.* **1** *adj.,* **2** *n., pl.* **nec·es·sar·ies.**

nec·tar   [nek'tər]   **1** in ancient Greek legends, the drink of the gods. **2** any delicious drink. **3** a sweet liquid found in many flowers. Bees gather nectar and make it into honey. *n.*

neigh·bour or **neigh·bor**   [nā'bər]   **1** someone who lives in the next house or nearby. **2** a person or thing that is near or next to another. **3** a fellow human being. *n.*

nerv·ous   [nėr'vəs]   **1** of the nerves. **2** easily excited or upset. **3** restless or uneasy; timid. *adj.* —**nerv'ous·ness,** *n.*

New Age   [njü' āj'] *or* [nü' āj']   a style of popular instrumental music designed to produce a relaxed mood.

New·found·land   [nyü found'lənd]   an island of eastern Canada; with the coast of Labrador, forms the province of Newfoundland. *n.*

nick·el   [nik'əl]   **1** a hard, silvery-white metal that is resistant to rust. **2** a coin containing nickel; a five-cent piece. *n.*

nine·ty   [nīn'tē]   nine times ten; 90. *n. pl.* **nine·ties;** *or adj.*

noise   [noiz]   **1** a sound that is not musical or pleasant; loud or harsh sound: *The noise kept me awake.* **2** any sound: *the noise of the rain on the roof. n.*
  ☞ *Etymology.* **Noise,** which originally meant a 'din' or 'loud disturbance', comes through French from Latin *nausea,* meaning 'seasickness', from the unpleasant din made by a shipful of seasick passengers.

nui·sance   [nyü'səns or nü'səns]   any thing or person that annoys, troubles, offends, or is disagreeable. *n.*

O ▼▼▼

of·fice   [of'is]   **1** the place in which the work of a business or profession is done. **2** the staff of persons carrying on work in an office. *n.*

of·fi·cial   [ə fish'əl *or* ō fish'əl]   **1** a person who holds a public position or who is in charge of some public work or duty. **2** having authority; coming from an authorized source. **1** *n.,* **2** *adj.* —**of·fi'cial·ly,** *adv.*

op·po·nent   [ə pō'nənt]   a person who is on the other side in a fight, game, or argument; a person fighting, struggling, or speaking against another: *He defeated his opponent in the election. n.*

or·bit   [ôr'bit]   **1** the path of a heavenly body, planet, or satellite around another body in space. **2** travel in orbit. **1** *n.,* **2** *v.*

o·rig·i·nal [ə rij′ə nəl] **1** belonging to the beginning; first; earliest. **2** fresh; novel; not done before or copied. **3** anything from which something else is copied, imitated, or translated: *The original of this picture is in Rome.* 1, 2 *adj.*, 3 *n.*

out·look [out′lůk′] **1** what seems likely to happen; a prospect. **2** a way of thinking about things; an attitude of mind; a point of view. *n.*

own·er·ship [ō′nər ship] being an owner; the possessing of something; the right of possession: *She claimed ownership of the abandoned boat.* *n.*

P

pan·ic [pan′ik] **1** a sudden fear that causes one to lose self-control; unreasoning fear. **2** affect or be affected with panic: *The driver panicked when his brakes failed.* 1 *n.*, 2 *v.* **pan·icked, pan·ick·ing.**

pa·tient [pā′shənt] **1** having patience; showing patience. **2** a person who is being treated by a doctor, dentist, etc. 1 *adj.*, 2 *n.*

pat·tern [pat′ərn] **1** an arrangement of forms and colours; a design. **2** a model or guide for something to be made. *n.*

pat·ty [pat′ē] **1** a small pie or filled pastry. **2** a small, flat, usually round cake of chopped food: *hamburger or chicken patties.* **3** a small, round, flat piece of candy: *a peppermint patty.* *n.*

pen·al·ty [pen′əl tē] **1** a punishment for breaking a law or rule. **2** a disadvantage placed on a side or player for breaking the rules of some game or contest. *n., pl.* **pen·al·ties.**

peo·ple [pē′pəl] **1** men, women, and children; persons. **2** a race or nation. *n.* **peo·pled, peo·pling.**

per·mit [pər mit′ *for 1*, pėr′mit *for 2*] **1** let; allow. **2** a formal written order giving permission to do something. 1 *v.*, **per·mit·ted, per·mit·ting;** 2 *n.*

perogy [pə rog′ē] dumplinglike pastries with a meat, cheese, or other filling. *n.*

per·son·al [pėr′sə nəl] **1** belonging to a person; private. **2** done in person; directly by oneself, not through others or by letter. *adj.*

pi·an·o [pē an′ō] a large musical instrument having strings that sound when struck by hammers operated by the keys on a keyboard. *n., pl.* **pi·an·os.**

pic·ture [pik′chər] **1** a drawing, painting, portrait, or photograph; a printed copy of any of these. **2** form a picture in the mind; imagine: *It is hard to picture life a hundred years ago.* 1 *n.*, 2 *v.*, **pic·tured, pic·tur·ing.**

pi·rate [pī′rit] **1** one who attacks and robs ships; a robber on the sea. **2** be a pirate. **3** sell or use a book, music, recording, etc. without the author's, inventor's, or owner's permission. 1 *n.*, 2, 3 *v.*, **pi·rat·ed, pi·rat·ing.**

---

hat, āge, fär; let, ēqual, tėrm; it, īce; hot, ōpen, ôrder oil, out; cup, pùt, rüle; əbove, takən, pencəl, lemən, circəs ch, child; ng, long; sh, ship th, thin; ᴛʜ, then; zh, measure

---

pit·y [pit′ē] **1** sympathy; sorrow for another's suffering or distress; a feeling for the sorrows of others. **2** feel pity for. 1 *n., pl.* **pit·ies;** 2 *v.*, **pit·ied, pit·y·ing.**
have or **take pity on,** show pity for.

plan·ta·tion [plan tā′shən] **1** a large farm or estate on which such crops as cotton, tobacco, or sugar are grown. **2** a large group of trees or other plants that have been planted. *n.*

play·er [plā′ər] **1** a person who plays. **2** a person who plays a musical instrument. *n.*

pleas·ant [plez′ənt] **1** that pleases; giving pleasure. **2** fair; not stormy. *adj.*

pleas·ure [plezh′ər] **1** the feeling of being pleased; delight; joy. **2** anything that amuses; sport; play. *n.*

pock·et [pok′it] **1** a small pouch or bag sewn into clothing for carrying money, or small articles. **2** put in one's pocket. **3** small enough to go in a pocket: *a pocket camera.* 1 *n.*, 2 *v.*, 3 *adj.*

po·em [pō′əm] **1** a piece of writing in which the words are arranged in lines having a regularly repeated accent. **2** a composition showing great beauty of language or thought. *n.*

poi·son [poi′zən] **1** a drug or other substance very dangerous to health and capable of causing death. **2** kill or harm by poison. 1 *n.*, 2 *v.*

pol·ish [pol′ish] **1** become smooth and shiny; take on a polish. **2** a substance used to give smoothness or shine. 1 *v.*, 2 *n.*

pos·i·tive [poz′ə tiv] **1** permitting no question; without doubt; sure. **2** a photographic print: *She kept the positives and sent back the negatives.* 1 *adj.*, 2 *n.* —**posi·tive·ly,** *adv.*

poutine [pü tēn′] *Cdn.* a Québec dish consisting of French fries topped with gravy and cheese. *n.*

pow·er·ful [pou′ər fəl] having great power or force; mighty; strong. *adj.*

pre·dict [pri dikt′] tell beforehand; prophesy. *v.*

pre·fer [pri fėr′] **1** like better; choose rather. **2** put forward; present. *v.*, **pre·ferred, pre·fer·ring.**

pre·pare [pri per′] **1** make ready; get ready: *He does his homework while his father prepares supper.* **2** make by a special process. *v.*, **pre·pared, pre·par·ing.**

pres·ent·ly [prez′ənt lē] **1** before long; soon. **2** at present; now. *adv.*

185

pres·i·dent [prez′ə dənt] **1** the chief officer of a company, college, society, club, etc. **2** Often, **President**, the highest officer of a republic. *n.*

prin·ci·pal [prin′sə pəl] **1** most important; chief; main. **2** a sum of money on which interest is paid. **1** *adj.*, **2** *n.*

prin·ci·ple [prin′sə pəl] **1** a fact or belief on which other ideas are based. **2** a rule of science explaining how things act. *n.*
☛ *Homonyms.* **Principle** is pronounced like **principal.**

pri·vate [prī′vit] **1** not for the public; for just a few special people or for one. **2** secret. *adj.*
—pri′vate·ly, *adv.*

prize [prīz] **1** a reward won or offered in a contest or competition. **2** worthy of a prize. **1** *n.*, **2** *adj.*
☛ *Homonyms.* **Prize** is pronounced like **pries.**

pro·ceed [prə sēd′] **1** go on after having stopped; move forward. **2** begin to carry on any activity. *v.*

pro·cess [prō′ses *or* pros′es] **1** a set of actions or changes in a special order. **2** treat or prepare by some special method: *This cloth has been processed to make it waterproof.* **1** *n.*, **2** *v.*

pro·duce [prə dyüs′ *or* prə düs′ *for 1*, prō′dyüs *or* prō′düs *for 2*] **1** make; bring into existence. **2** what is produced; the yield. **1** *v.*, **pro·duced, pro·duc·ing;** **2** *n.*

pro·fes·sion [prə fesh′ən] **1** an occupation requiring special education, such as law, medicine, or teaching. **2** the people engaged in such an occupation: *The medical profession favours this law.* *n.*

pro·fes·sor [prə fes′ər] **1** a teacher of the highest rank in college or university. **2** *Informal.* any teacher at a college or university. *n.*

pro·gress [prō′gres *or* prog′res *for 1*, prə gres′ *for 2*] **1** advance; growth; development; improvement. **2** get better; advance; develop. **1** *n.*, **2** *v.*

pro·pel·ler [prə pel′ər] a device with revolving blades, for propelling boats and aircraft. *n.*

pro·tec·tive [prə tek′tiv] **1** protecting; being a defence. **2** preventing injury to those around: *a protective device on a machine.* *adj.*

pro·trac·tor [prō trak′tər] an instrument for drawing or measuring angles. *n.*

pro·vide [prə vid′] **1** supply; furnish. **2** arrange in advance; state as a condition beforehand: *Our club's rules provide that dues must be paid monthly.* *v.*, **pro·vid·ed, pro·vid·ing.**

publish [pub′lish] **1** prepare and offer a book, paper, map, piece of music, etc. for sale or distibution. **2** make publicly or generally known: *Don't publish the faults of your friends.* *v.*

pu·pa [pyü′pə] **1** a stage between the larva and the adult in the development of many insects. In the pupa stage the insect is enclosed in a case. **2** an insect in this stage. *n., pl.* **pu·pae** [pyü′pē] *or* **pu·pas.**

pur·chase [pėr′chəs] **1** get by paying a price; buy. **2** the act of buying. **1** *v.*, **pur·chased, pur·chas·ing;** **2** *n.* **—pur′chas·er,** *n.*

puz·zle [puz′əl] **1** a hard problem. **2** a problem or task to be done for fun. **3** make unable to understand something; perplex. **1, 2** *n.*, **3** *v.*, **puz·zled, puz·zling.**

Q

quote [kwōt] **1** repeat the exact words of; give words or a passage from. **2** a quotation. **1** *v.*, **quot·ed, quot·ing;** **2** *n.*

R ▼▼▼

rap [rap] **1** a quick, light blow; a light, sharp knock. **2** a type of popular music consisting of rhyming verse, chanted or shouted to a strong, repetitive beat. *n.*

re·al·ly [rē′ə lē *or* rē′lē] **1** actually; truly; in fact. **2** an expression of surprise, disbelief, or disapproval: *Really, Tom? You must be kidding!* **1** *adv.*, **2** *interj.*

re·cent [rē′sənt] **1** done, made, or happening not long ago. **2** not long past; modern: *a recent period of history.* *adj.* **—re′cent·ly,** *adv.*

redial [rē dī′əl] a feature of a telephone system allowing users to enter a telephone number again without re-entering each digit, simply by pressing a special button. *n.*

re—en·try [rē en′trē] an entering again or returning, especially of a rocket or spacecraft into Earth's atmosphere after flight in outer space. *n.*

ref·u·gee [ref′yə jē′] a person who flees for refuge or safety, especially to a foreign country, in time of war, persecution, or disaster: *Many refugees came from Europe to Canada.* *n.*

re·lease [ri lēs′] **1** let go. **2** let loose; set free. **3** relieve. **4** letting go; setting free. **1-3** *v.*, **re·leased, re·leas·ing;** **4** *n.*

re·lief [ri lēf′] **1** the lessening of, or freeing from, a pain, burden, difficulty, etc. **2** a change of persons on duty. *n.*

re·spon·si·ble [ri spon′sə bəl] **1** obliged or expected to account for; accountable; answerable. **2** deserving credit or blame. *adj.*

re·view [ri vyü′] **1** study again; look at again. **2** studying again. **1** *v.*, **2** *n.*

rhyme [rīm] **1** sound alike in the last part. **2** a word or line having the same last sound as another. 1 *v.*, **rhymed, rhym•ing;** 2 *n.*

ro•ma•nes•co [rō′mə nes′kō] a vegetable that is a cross of cauliflower, broccoli, and cabbage. *n.*

S

san•dal [san′dəl] a shoe made of a sole and a strap; any of various kinds of low-cut shoes, slippers, etc. *n.*

sa•mo•sa [sə mō′sə] an East Indian dish consisting of spicy meat or vegetables in pastry. *n.*

SASE self-addressed stamped envelope.

sat•is•fac•tion [sat′is fak′shən] **1** the condition of being satisfied, or pleased and contented. **2** anything that makes us feel pleased or contented: *It is a great satisfaction to have things turn out just the way you want. n.*

sat•is•fy [sat′is fī′] **1** give enough to; fulfil desires, hopes, or demands; put an end to wants or needs. **2** pay; make right. *v.*, **sat•is•fied, sat•is•fy•ing.**

scale [skāl] **1** one of the thin, flat, hard plates forming the outer covering of some fishes, snakes, and lizards. **2** remove scales from. 1 *n.*, 2 *v.*, **scaled, scal•ing**

sci•en•tist [sī′ən tist] a person who has expert knowledge of some branch of science. Persons specially trained in and familiar with the facts and laws of such fields of study as biology, chemistry, mathematics, physics, geology, and astronomy are scientists. *n.*

score•board [skôr bôrd] a large, often electrically-operated board for displaying the score of a game or match. *n.*

scor•pi•on [skôr′pē ən] a small animal belonging to the same group as the spider and having a poisonous sting at the end of its tail. *n.*

scur•ry [skėr′ē] **1** run quickly; scamper; hurry. **2** a hasty running or hurrying. 1 *v.*, **scur•ried, scur•ry•ing;** 2 *n.*

sea•son [sē′zən] **1** one of the four periods of the year; spring, summer, autumn, or winter. **2** any period of time marked by something special. **3** add flavour to. 1, 2 *n.*, 3 *v.*

sen•si•tive [sen′sə tiv] **1** receiving impressions readily. **2** easily affected or influenced. *adj.*

sen•tence [sen′təns] **1** a word or group of words having a subject and a predicate. **2** pronounce punishment on. 1 *n.*, 2 *v.*, **sen•tenced, sen•tenc•ing.**

hat, āge, fär; let, ēqual, tėrm; it, īce; hot, ōpen, ôrder oil, out; cup, pùt, rüle; ə above, takən, pencəl, lemən, circəs
ch, child; ng, long; sh, ship
th, thin; ᴛʜ, then; zh, measure

sep•a•rate [sep′ə rāt′ *for 1,* sep′ə rit *for 2*] **1** be between; keep apart; divide. **2** apart from others; divided; not joined; individual; single: *in a separate room, separate seats, the separate parts of a machine.* 1 *v.*, **sep•a•rat•ed, sep•a•rat•ing;** 2 *adj.* —**sep′a•rate•ly,** *adv.*

ser•geant [sär′jənt] **1** a rank in the armed forces, next above corporal. **2** a similar rank in a police force. *n.*

se•ri•al [sē′rē əl] **1** a story presented one part at a time in a magazine or newspaper, or on radio or television. **2** of a series; arranged in a series. 1 *n.*, 2 *adj.*
☛ *Homonyms.* **Serial** is pronounced like **cereal.**

se•ries [sē′rēz] **1** a number of similar things in a row. **2** a number of things placed one after another: *in alphabetical series.* **3** a number of things or events happening one after the other: *A series of rainy days spoiled their vacation. n., pl.* **ser•ies.**

se•ri•ous [sē′rē əs] **1** thoughtful; grave. **2** important; needing thought. *adj.* —**se′ri•ous•ness,** *n.*

ser•vant [sėr′vənt] **1** a person employed in a household. **2** a person employed by another. *n.*

shall [shal; *unstressed,* shəl] an auxiliary verb used: **1** in questions with *I* or *we* to ask what one is to do. **2** in statements with *you, he, she,* or *they,* to show that a person has to do something. *v.*, past tense **should.**

shelves [shelvz] plural of **shelf.** *n.*

shoot [shüt] **1** send with force or speed at a target. **2** move suddenly and rapidly. **3** take a picture with a camera; photograph. *v.*, **shot, shoot•ing.**

short•stop [shôrt′stop′] a baseball player stationed between second and third base. *n.*

shout [shout] **1** call or cry loudly and vigorously. **2** a loud, vigorous call or cry. 1 *v.*, 2 *n.*

shut•ter [shut′ər] **1** a movable cover, usually made of wood, for a window. **2** a movable cover, slide, etc. for closing an opening. The device that opens and closes in front of the film in a camera is the shutter. *n.*

sign [sīn] **1** any mark or thing used to mean, represent, or point out something. **2** put one's name on; write one's name. **3** an inscribed board, space, etc. serving for advertisement, information, etc. 1, 3 *n.*, 2 *v.*

187

sig·na·ture [sig′nə chər] **1** one's name written by oneself, as on a cheque or letter. **2** in music, the signs printed at the beginning of a staff to show the key and time of a piece of music. *n.*

skill [skil] **1** ability gained by practice or knowledge; expertness. **2** an ability that can be learned: *One must master the basic language skills. n.*

slam [slam] **1** shut with force and noise; close with a bang. **2** throw, push, hit, or move with force. *v.*, **slammed, slam·ming.**

sleigh [slā] **1** a carriage or cart mounted on runners for use on snow or ice. **2** a plaything consisting of a framework of boards mounted on metal or wooden runners, for use on snow or ice: *The children had great fun playing with their sleighs. n.*

slight [slīt] **1** not much; not important; small. **2** slighting treatment; an act showing neglect or lack of respect: *She suffered many slights from her sisters.* **1** *adj.*, **2** *n.*

smash [smash] **1** break into pieces with violence and noise. **2** a violent breaking or shattering; crash. **1** *v.*, **2** *n.*

soc·cer [sok′ər] a game played between two teams of eleven in which the players try to kick a round ball into the goal at the opponents' end of the field. The ball may be struck with any part of the body except the hands and arms. *n.*

so·cial [sō′shəl] **1** of dealing with human beings in their relations to each other. **2** living or liking to live with others. **3** a social gathering or party. **1**, **2** *adj.*, **3** *n.* **—so′cial·ly**, *adv.*

soft [soft] **1** smooth; pleasant to the touch; not rough or coarse. **2** softly; gently. **1** *adj.*, **2** *adv.* **—soft′ly**, *adv.* **—soft′ness**, *n.*

some·day [sum′dā′] at some future time. *adv.*

sound¹ [sound] **1** what is or can be heard. **2** make a sound or noise: *The wind sounds like an animal howling.* **1** *n.*, **2** *v.*

sound² [sound] **1** healthy; free from disease. **2** strong; safe; secure. *adj.*, **—sound′ly**, *adv.* **—sound′ness**, *n.*

sound bite [sound′ bit′] a short clip on a news program, featuring a brief statement or part of a statement by a politician, reporter, celebrity, etc. especially a recorded one inserted into many broadcasts or one that is often quoted. *n.*

source [sôrs] **1** a person or place from which anything comes or is obtained: *A newspaper gets news from many sources. Mines are the chief source of diamonds.* **2** the beginning of a river or brook; fountain; spring. *n.*

spar·kle [spär′kəl] **1** send out little sparks. **2** a little spark. **3** shine; glitter; flash. **1**, **3** *v.*, **spar·kled, spar·kling; 2** *n.*

speech [spēch] **1** the act of speaking; talk. **2** a manner of speaking. *n.*

spir·it [spir′it] **1** the soul. **2** the moral, religious, or emotional part of human nature. **3** Often, **spirits**, *pl.* a state of mind; disposition; temper. *n.* **out of spirits**, sad; gloomy.

stage [stāj] **1** one step or degree in a process; a period of development. **2** the raised platform in a theatre on which the actors perform. **3** put on a stage or arrange. **1**, **2** *n.*, **3** *v.*, **staged, stag·ing.**

stand·ard [stan′dərd] **1** anything taken as a basis of comparison; a model; an accepted level of quality, size, etc.: *The builder's work was not up to standard.* **2** of the accepted or normal size, amount, power, quality, etc. **1** *n.*, **2** *adj.*

star·va·tion [stär vā′shən] **1** starving. **2** suffering from extreme hunger; being starved. *n.*

sto·len [stō′lən] the past participle of **steal.** *v.*

stor·age [stô′rij] **1** the act or fact of storing goods. **2** a place for storing: *She has put her furniture in storage.* **3** the cost of storing: *She paid $300 storage on her furniture. n.*

sto·ry [stô′rē] **1** an account of some happening or group of happenings. **2** *Informal.* a falsehood: *That boy is a liar; he tells stories. n.*, *pl.* **sto·ries.**

straight [strāt] **1** without a bend or curve: *a straight line.* **2** in a line; directly. **3** frank; honest; upright. **1**, **3** *adj.*, **2** *adv.*

strait [strāt] **1** a narrow channel connecting two larger bodies of water. **2** **straits**, *pl.* difficulty; need; distress: *He was in desperate straits for money. n.*

stray [strā] **1** lose one's way; wander; roam. **2** wandering; lost. **3** turn from the right course; go wrong. **1**, **3** *v.*, **2** *adj.*

strip¹ [strip] **1** make bare or naked; undress. **2** take off the covering of: *The boy stripped the skin from a banana.* **3** rob: *Thieves stripped the house of everything valuable. v.*, **stripped, strip·ping.**

strip² [strip] **1** a long, narrow, flat, piece of cloth, paper, bark, etc. **2** a long, narrow runway for airplanes to take off from and land on. *n.*

stroke¹ [strōk] **1** an act of striking; a blow; a hit. **2** a sound made by striking. *n.*

stroke² [strōk] **1** move the hand gently along: *He likes to stroke his kitten.* **2** such a movement: *She brushed away the crumbs with one stroke.* **1** *v.*, **stroked, strok·ing; 2** *n.*

stu·dent [styü′dənt *or* stü′dənt] **1** a person who is studying in a school, college, or university: *That high school has 3000 students.* **2** a person who studies: *She is a student of birds. n.*

stud·y [stud′ē] **1** the effort to learn by reading or thinking: *After an hour's hard study he knew his lesson.* **2** try to learn. **3** examine carefully: *We studied the map to find the shortest way home.* **1** *n.*, *pl.* **stud·ies;** **2** *v.*, **stud·ied, stud·y·ing.**

sub·ma·rine [sub′mə rēn′ *for 1*, sub′mə rēn′ *for 2*] **1** a boat that can go under water. **2** placed, growing, or used below the surface of the sea. **1** *n.*, **2** *adj.*

sub·sti·tute [sub′stə tyüt′ *or* sub′stə tüt′] **1** something used instead of something else; a person taking the place of another: *A substitute taught our class today.* **2** put in the place of another: *We substituted brown sugar for molasses in these cookies.* **1** *n.*, **2** *v.*, **sub·sti·tut·ed, sub·sti·tut·ing.**

sub·tract [səb trakt′] take away. *v.*

suc·cess [sək ses′] **1** a favourable result; a wished-for ending; good fortune. **2** a person or thing that succeeds: *The circus was a great success.* **3** the result; outcome; fortune; *What success did you have in finding a new apartment?* *n.*
—**suc·cess′ful,** *adj.*

sug·ar [shùg′ər] **1** a sweet substance made chiefly from sugar cane or sugar beets. **2** put sugar in; sweeten with sugar. **1** *n.*, **2** *v.*

sug·gest [sə jest′ *or* səg jest′] **1** bring to mind; call up the thought of: *The thought of summer suggests swimming and hot weather.* **2** propose: *She suggested a swim, and we all agreed.* **3** show in an indirect way; hint: *His yawns suggested that he would like to go to bed.* *v.*

suit·a·ble [sü′tə bəl] right for the occasion; fitting; proper: *A simple outfit is suitable for school wear. The park gives the children a suitable playground.* *adj.*

sunk·en [sung′kən] **1** sunk. **2** submerged; under water. **3** fallen in; hollow: *sunken eyes.* *adj.*

surf [sėrf] search casually for interesting material on the Internet. *v.*

sur·prise [sər prīz′] **1** a feeling caused by something unexpected. **2** catch unprepared; come upon suddenly. **1** *n.*, **2** *v.*, **sur·prised, sur·pris·ing.**

swirl [swėrl] **1** move or drive along with a twisting motion; whirl. **2** a swirling movement; a whirl; an eddy. **1** *v.*, **2** *n.*

switch [swich] **1** stroke; lash. **2** a device for making or breaking a connection in an electric circuit. **3** change; exchange: *to switch places.* **1, 2** *n.*, **3** *v.*

syr·up or **sir·up** [sėr′əp *or* sir′əp] a sweet, thick liquid. *n.*

sys·tem [sis′təm] **1** a set of things or parts forming a whole: *a mountain system, a railway system, the digestive system.* **2** a plan; scheme; method: *We have a system for organizing our records and cassettes.* *n.*

hat, āge, fär; let, ēqual, tėrm; it, īce; hot, ōpen, ôrder
oil, out; cup, pùt, rüle; above, takən, pencəl, lemən, circəs
ch, child; ng, long; sh, ship
th, thin; ᴛʜ, then; zh, measure

T

tan·ge·los [tan′ jə lōz *or* tan jel′ōz] a citrus fruit developed by crossing the grapefruit and the tangerine, now grown in several varieties. *n.*

tar·get [tär′git] **1** a mark for shooting at; something aimed at. **2** an aim one tries to achieve; goal; objective: *The target for the fund-raising drive was $10 000.* *n.*

taught [tot] the past tense and past participle of **teach**: *Miss Jones taught my mother. She has taught music for many years.* *v.*

team·mate [tēm′mat′] a fellow member of a team. *n.*

team·work [tēm′wėrk′] the acting together of a number of people to make the work of the group successful and effective: *Teamwork makes hard jobs easier.* *n.*

tel·e·phone [tel′ə fōn′] **1** an apparatus, system, or process for sending and receiving sound or speech over distances. **2** talk by means of a telephone; send a message by telephone. **1** *n.*, **2** *v.*, **tel·e·phoned, tel·e·phon·ing.**

ten·nis [ten′is] a game played by two or four players on a special court, in which a ball is hit back and forth over a net with a racket. *n.*

ten·sion [ten′shən] **1** a stretching. **2** a stretched condition; a taut state: *The tension of the bow gives speed to the arrow.* **3** mental strain: *The students felt a lot of tension waiting to hear the exam results.* *n.*

ter·rif·ic [tə rif′ic] **1** causing great fear; terrifying: *A terrific earthquake shook Japan.* **2** very unusual; remarkable; extraordinary: *A terrific hot spell ruined many of the crops.* *adj.*

TGIF *Informal.* Thank Goodness It's Friday.

the·a·tre [thē′ə tər] **1** a place where plays or other stage performances are acted or where motion pictures are shown. **2** plays; writing, acting in, or producing plays; the drama: *He was interested in the theatre and tried to write plays himself.* *n.*

them·selves [ᴛʜem selvz′] **1** a form used instead of **them** when referring back to the subject of the sentence: *Their boots were muddy, so they washed them and then washed themselves.* **2** a form of **they** or **them** used to make a statement stronger: *The teachers themselves said that the test was too hard.* *pron.*

they've [ᴛʜāv] they have.

thou·sand [thou′zend] ten hundred; 1000. *n.* or *adj.*

threw [thrü]   the past tense of **throw**: *He threw a stone and ran away.* *v.*

ti·tle [tī′təl]   **1** the name of a book, poem, picture, song, etc. **2** the first-place position; a championship: *She won the tennis title at school.* *n.*

toast[1] [tōst]   **1** a slice or slices of bread browned by heat **2** brown by heat. **1** *n.*, **2** *v.*

toast[2] [tōst]   **1** take a drink and wish good fortune to; drink to the health of. **2** a person having many admirers: *She used to be the toast of the town.* **1** *v.*, **2** *n.*

toll–free [tōl frē]   describing a telephone number that people living in any area can call for free. The person or company having the number pays the phone company a special fee for this service: *For more information call the toll-free number listed below.* *adj.*

tor·ture [tôr′chər]   **1** the act of inflicting very severe pain. Torture used to be widely used to make people give evidence about crimes, or to make them confess. **2** cause very severe pain to. **1** *n.*, **2** *v.*, **tor·tured, tor·tur·ing.**

to·tal [tō′təl]   **1** whole; entire: *The total cost of the house and land will be $95 000.* **2** the whole amount: *His expenses reached a total of $100. Add the different sums to get the total.* **3** find the sum of; add: *Total that column of figures.* **1** *adj.*, **2** *n.*, **3** *v.*, **to·talled** or **to·taled, to·tal·ling** or **to·tal·ing.** —**to′tal·ly,** *adv.*

tow·er·ing [tou′ə ring]   **1** very high: *a towering peak.* **2** very great: *Making electricity from nuclear power is a towering achievement.* **3** very violent: *a towering rage.* *adj.*

trag·ic [traj′ik]   **1** of tragedy; having to do with tragedy: *a tragic actor, a tragic poet.* **2** very sad; dreadful: *a tragic death, a tragic accident.* *adj.*

trans·fer [trans′fèr; *also* trans fèr′ *for 1 and 2*]   **1** convey or remove from one person or place to another; hand over. **2** convey a drawing, design, pattern from one surface to another: *You transfer the embroidery design from the paper to cloth by pressing it with a warm iron.* *v.*, **trans·ferred, trans·fer·ring.**

trans·form [trans fôrm′]   **1** change in form or appearance: *The blizzard transformed the bushes into glittering mounds of snow.* **2** change in condition, nature, or character: *A generator transforms mechanical energy into electricity.* *v.*

trans·for·ma·tion [trans′fər mā′shən]   transforming or being transformed: *We were amazed at the transformation of an honest man into a thief.* *n.*

trans·late [trans lāt′, tranz lāt′, *or* tranz′lāt]   **1** change from one language into another: *to translate a book from French into English.* **2** change into other words especially in order to explain the meaning of: *The scientist translated her idea into language we could understand.* *v.*, **trans·lat·ed, trans·lat·ing.**

trans·par·ent [trans per′ənt *or* trans par′ənt]   **1** transmitting light so that something behind or beyond can be distinctly seen: *Window glass is transparent.* **2** easily seen through or detected: *The boy offered a transparent excuse.* *adj.*

trans·por·ta·tion [trans′pər tā′shən]   **1** transporting or being transported: *The railway allows free transportation for a certain amount of a passenger's baggage.* **2** a means of transport. *n.*

trav·el [trav′əl]   **1** go from one place to another: *She is travelling in Europe this summer.* **2** going in trains, airplanes, ships, cars, etc. from one place to another. **3** move; proceed; pass: *Sound travels in waves.* **1, 3** *v.*, **trav·elled** or **trav·eled, trav·el·ling** or **trav·el·ing; 2** *n.*

tri·ath·lon [trīath′lon]   an Olympic sport in which athletes compete in swimming, bicycling, and running. *n.*

trick [trik]   **1** something done to deceive or cheat. **2** a clever act; a feat of skill. **3** play pranks. **1, 2** *n.*, **3** *v.*

trip [trip]   **1** a journey; voyage. **2** stumble. **3** a loss of footing; a stumble. **1, 3** *n.*, **2** *v.*, **tripped, trip·ping.**

Tues·day [tyüz′dā′ *or* tüz′dā, tyüz′dē *or* tüz′dē]   the third day of the week, following Monday. *n.*
☛ *Etymology.* **Tuesday** developed from Old English *Tiwesdæg*, meaning 'day of Tīw', Tīw was the Germanic god of war.

tun·nel [tun′əl]   **1** any underground passage, such as an underground way for a railway, a horizontal passage in a mine, or an animal's burrow. **2** make a tunnel: *The mole tunnelled in the ground.* **1** *n.*, **2** *v.*, **tun·nelled** or **tun·neled, tun·nel·ling** or **tun·nel·ing.**

type [tīp]   **1** a kind, class, or group alike in some way. **2** a piece of metal or wood having on its upper surface a raised letter or figure for use in printing. **3** write with a typewriter. **1, 2** *n.*, **3** *v.* **typed, typ·ing.**

U ▼▼▼

ug·li·ness [ug′lē nis]   an ugly quality or appearance; being ugly. *n.*

ultralight aircraft [ul′ trə līt′ er′ kraft′]   a motorized hang glider; small, very light, open airplane with one suspended seat. *n.*

ul·tra·sound   [ul′ trə sound′]   **1** ultrasonic waves. **2** a single ultrasonographic examination using sound waves to visualize deep structures in the body: *I had an ultrasound yesterday.*

un·der·stand   [un′dər stand′]   **1** get the meaning of; comprehend: *Now I understand the teacher's question.*   **2** know well; know how to deal with: *A good teacher understands children.*   **3** be informed; learn: *I understand that he is leaving town.*   *v.*, **un·der·stood, un·der·stand·ing.**

un·em·ploy·ment   [un′em ploi′mənt]   a lack of employment; being out of work.   *n.*

un·hap·py   [un hap′ē]   **1** sad; sorrowful: *an unhappy face.*   **2** unlucky: *an unhappy accident.* **3** not suitable: *an unhappy selection of colours.*   *adj.*, **un·hap·pi·er, un·hap·pi·est.** —**unhap′pi·ly,** *adv.* —**un·hap′pi·ness,** *n.*

un·known   [un′nōn *for 1,* un nōn′ *for 2*]   **1** not known; not familiar; strange; unexplored: *an unknown country, an unknown number.*   **2** a person or thing that is unknown: *The diver descended into the unknown.*   1 *adj.,* 2 *n.*

un·less   [un les′]   except on the condition that; if not.   *conj.*

un·load   [un lōd′]   **1** remove a load.   **2** discharge a cargo.   *v.*

un·paid   [un pād′]   not paid.   *adj.*

un·pop·u·lar   [un pop′yə lər]   not generally liked; disliked.   *adj.*

ur·gent   [ėr′jənt]   demanding immediate action or attention; pressing: *an urgent duty, an urgent message.*   *adj.*

V ▼▼▼

val·u·able   [val′yü ə bəl *or* val′yə bəl]   **1** having value; being worth something: *valuable information, a valuable friend.*   **2** Usually, **valuables,** *pl.* articles of value: *She keeps her jewellery and other valuables in a safe.*   1 *adj.,* 2 *n.*

var·y   [ver′ē *or* var′ē]   **1** change; make or become different: *The driver can vary the speed of an automobile. The weather varies.*   **2** be different; differ.   *v.*, **var·ied, var·y·ing.** ☛ *Homonyms.* **Vary** [ver′ē] is pronounced like **very.**

veg·e·ta·ble   [vej′ə tə bəl *or* vej′tə bəl]   **1** a part of a plant, such as leaves, seeds, or roots, and sometimes fruit, used for food and usually eaten with the main part of the meal.   **2** of, having to do with, or like plants: *the vegetable kingdom, vegetable life.*   1 *n.,* 2 *adj.*

ver·y   [ver′ē]   **1** much; greatly; extremely. **2** absolutely; exactly.   *adv.* ☛ *Homonyms.* **Very** is pronounced like **vary** [ver′ē].

hat, āge, fär; let, ēqual, tėrm; it, īce; hot, ōpen, ôrder
oil, out; cup, pùt, rüle; əbove, takən, pencəl, lemən, circəs
ch, child; ng, long; sh, ship
th, thin; ᴛʜ, then; zh, measure

video arcade   [vid′ē ō är kād′]   a public place where people can go to play a large variety of coin-operated video games.   *n.*

vid·e·o·gra·phy   [vid′ē og′ rə fē]   videos as a group, the study of videos, or the business and art of making videos.   *v.*

virtual reality   [vėr′ chü əl rē al′ə tē]   *Computer technology.* a highly effective simulation of reality achieved through video and audio programming, in which the user or viewer actually experiences the physical sensations associated with the scenes, events, environment, etc. represented on the computer system, and can interact with them as though they were real.   *n.*

vis·i·ble   [viz′ə bəl]   **1** that can be seen: *The shore was barely visible through the fog.*   **2** apparent; obvious: *The tramp had no visible means of support.*   *adj.*

vi·tal   [vī′təl]   **1** having to do with or necessary to life: *Eating is a vital function.*   **2 vitals,** *pl.* parts or organs necessary to life.   **3** full of life and spirit; lively: *That successful sports club is a very vital organization.*   1, 3 *adj.,* 2 *n.*

W ▼▼▼

wade   [wād]   **1** walk through water, snow, sand, mud, or anything that hinders free motion.   **2** make one's way with difficulty: *Must I wade through that dull book?*   *v.*, **wad·ed, wad·ing.**

wash   [wosh]   **1** clean with water: *to wash one's face, to wash dishes, to wash clothes.*   **2** carry or be carried along or away by water or other liquid.   *v.*

wealth·y   [wel′thē]   having wealth; rich.   *adj.*, **wealth·i·er, wealth·i·est.**

weigh   [wā]   **1** find the mass of: *I weighed myself this morning.*   **2** bend by weight; burden: *The boughs of the apple tree are weighed down with fruit.* **3** balance in the mind; consider carefully: *He weighs his words before speaking.*   **4** lift up an anchor: *The ship weighed anchor and sailed away.*   *v.*

weird   [wērd]   **1** unearthly; mysterious; wild; strange.   **2** *Informal.* odd; fantastic.   *adj.*

whether   [weᴛʜ′ər *or* hweᴛʜ′ər]   **1** a word used in expressing a choice or an alternative: *Whether we go or whether we stay matters very little.*   **2** if: *He asked whether he should finish the work.*   **3** either: *Whether sick or well, she is always cheerful.*   *conj.*

whole   [hōl]   **1** having all its parts; complete.   **2** all of a thing; the total.   **3** not injured or broken.   1, 3 *adj.,* 2 *n.*

whose [hüz] the possessive form of **who** and of **which**: of whom; of which. *pron.*
☞ *Homonyms.* **Whose** is pronounced like **who's.**

wick·ed [wik'id] **1** bad; evil; sinful: *wicked weeds.* **2** mischievous; playfully sly: *a wicked smile.* **3** *Informal.* unpleasant; severe: *A wicked storm swept through the northern part of the province.* *adj.*

wide·ly [wīd'lē] **1** to a wide extent: *a widely distributed plant, a musician who is widely known, to be widely read.* **2** very; extremely: *The witnesses gave two widely different accounts of the quarrel.* *adv.*

win [win] **1** to be successful over others; get victory or success. **2** a success; victory. 1 *v.,* **won, win·ning;** 2 *n.*

won·der [wun'dər] **1** a strange and surprising thing or event. **2** feel wonder. **3** be curious about; wish to know. 1 *n.,* 2, 3 *v.*

wood [wùd] **1** the hard substance beneath the bark of trees and shrubs. **2** made of wood; wooden: *a wood house.* **3** Often, **woods,** *pl.* an area with a large number of growing trees; forest: *looking for flowers in the woods.* 1, 3 *n.,* 2 *adj.*
out of the woods, out of danger or difficulty.
☞ *Homonyms.* **Wood** is pronounced like **would.**

World Wide Web [wèrld' wīd' web'] an unlimited series of interconnected documents on various subjects, that can be reached via the Internet. In each document, or file, there are specially marked words which the user can click on [or 'select'] to open up related files. The files are created and put on the Web by various groups and individuals, each of whom has its own site or address on the Web. *n.*

worry [wèr'ē] **1** feel anxious; be uneasy: *She worries about little things. She will worry if we are late.* **2** care; anxiety; trouble; uneasiness. 1 *v.,* **wor·ries, wor·ried, wor·ry·ing;** 2 *n.*

worst [wèrst] **1** most ill: *This is the worst I've been since I got sick.* **2** most bad; most evil: *None of them are good, but he's the worst of the lot.* **3** in the worst manner or degree: *He acts worst when he's tired.* 1, 2 *adj.,* 3 *adv.*

worth·less [wèrth'lis] without worth; good-for-nothing; useless. *adj.*

would [wùd; *unstressed,* wəd] the past tense of **will** used: **1** to introduce a very polite request: *Would you please close the window?* **2** to express an unlikely or an impossible condition: *If I asked whether I could go, she would say no.* **3** to express action done again and again: *When we were small, we would spend hours playing in the sand.* *v.*
☞ *Homonyms.* **Would** is pronounced like **wood.**

would·n't [wùd'ənt] would not.

wrin·kle [ring'kəl] **1** an irregular ridge or fold; crease. **2** make a wrinkle or wrinkles in. 1 *n.,* 2 *v.,* **wrin·kled, wrin·kling.**

write [rīt] **1** make letters or words with pen, pencil, chalk, etc.: **2** mark with letters or words. **3** make up stories, books, etc. compose: *She writes for the magazine.* *v.* **wrote, writ·ten, writ·ing.**

Y ▼▼▼

your·self [yür self'; *unstressed,* yər self'] **1** a form used instead of **you** when referring back to the subject of the sentence: *Did you hurt yourself?* **2** a form of **you** used to make a statement stronger: *You yourself know the story is not true.* **3** your real or true self: *Now that your cold is better, you'll feel like yourself again.* *pron., pl.* **your·selves.**

Z ▼▼▼

ze·ro [zē'rō] **1** nought; the figure 0. **2** of or at zero. **3** nothing. 1, 3 *n., pl.* **ze·ros** or **ze·roes;** 2 *adj.,*
☞ *Etymology.* **Zero** came into English from an Italian word which in turn was taken from the Arabic word *sifr,* meaning 'empty'. It is related to **cipher.**